Beyond the
Enchanted Bridge

I hope you
enjoy your visit
to Scarecrow Land!

Andy Oliver

9/20/07

Martha's Enchanted Bridge

Beyond the

Enchanted Bridge

A Visit to
Scarecrow Land

Story & Photographs by

Andrew Oliver

A-PP
Adams-Pomeroy Press
Albany, Wisconsin

Published by: A-PP   Adams-Pomeroy Press
                             P.O. Box 189
                             Albany, Wisconsin 53502

The characters in the book are fictitious. Any similarity to real persons living or dead is conicidental and not intended by the author.

Printed in the United States of America
First Printing 2002

Cover by Robert Howard Graphic Design

Publisher's Cataloging-in-Publication
(Provided by Quality Books, Inc.)

Oliver, Andrew (Andrew Thomas)
        Beyond the enchanted bridge : a visit to Scarecrow
    Land / story & photographs by Andrew Oliver. -- 1st ed.

        p. cm.
        SUMMARY: What is ten-year-old Martha to do when her
    brother disappears on a rocking horse that turns into a
    real horse and takes him to Scarecrow Land? Join Martha
    as she meets strange characters and encounters
    unexpected situations in her search.
        Audience: Grades 4-7
        LCCN 2001135182
        ISBN 0-9661009-3-X

        1. Scarecrows--Juvenile fiction. 2. Agriculture--
    Juvenile fiction. 3.Wisconsin--Juvenile fiction. 4.
    Cheese--Wisconsin--History--Juvenile fiction.
    [1.Scarecrows--Fiction. 2. Farm life--Fiction.
    3. Wisconsin--Fiction. 4. Cheese--Fiction. 5. Stories in
    rhyme.]   I. Title.

    PZ8.3O492Be 2002   [Fic]
                              QBI01-700979

To Mary Rowley,
an exceptional English woman,
with whom I taught in Nigeria.
I knew her as a paragon of moral character and wisdom
who demonstrated respect for every man, woman, and child,
however poor, however lacking, however humble.

Acknowledgments

I am thankful to those wonderfully positive people who helped in so many various ways with this book. Without them, I never would have finished my tale.

First and foremost, I am indebted to Catherine Blakemore, my publisher, for her untiring dedication to content, format, and, ironically, punctuation, spelling, and usage. But even before I knew Catherine was to offer to publish my book, before I even entertained the thought that she might be interested, she offered to read my story. Thereupon, she offered excellent suggestions for changes, which I heeded. Once again she read my story. I was delighted a few weeks later when she called me with an offer to publish *Beyond the Enchanted Bridge: A Visit to Scarecrow Land.*

Similarly, I wish to thank my lifelong friend, Glenn Holtsapple, who, not once but twice, read my story long before editing and reworking. It was his enthusiasm more than anything else that kept me working on it, that led me to believe maybe it was something people might enjoy as much as I enjoyed writing it.

And I want to say thanks to Lisa Kay Hauser, with her ear for music and meter, for editing my story. It was by chance that I asked her to look at my manuscript while I was attending her book signing for *Turn Back Time.* I was impressed when the award-winning author began reading it on the spot, laughing with enjoyment—and this too encouraged me. Her subsequent suggestions for changes here and there were excellent and contributed greatly to my efforts at poetry.

I am likewise indebted to others—from children to librarians to teachers—who read my manuscript, offered suggestions, wrote endorsements, or provided feedback.

Of course I am grateful to Blake and Denise Speaker, whose scarecrow, Buddy, came home with me, figuratively anyway, to assist me in writing my story. I thank the Speakers for allowing me to photograph their scarecrow, and I thank the many others who graciously permitted me to photograph their scarecrows, horses, barns, cattle, windmills, and so on. I am thankful to the people of Shullsburg for sponsoring Cheese Fest, for providing a setting in which my story could come to life.

Finally, I am thankful to farm people, past and present, who provided the spiritual ethos of my story's life. I hope my story, in some little way, deepens the reader's appreciation for the unending work farmers endure, while always facing the challenges and uncertainties of changing times. Likewise, I am indebted to those in the cheesemaking industry. Though the number of local cheese factories declines, cheesemakers, through determined effort and talent, have persevered, helping preserve farming as a way of life—a very special way of life.

Photographs

Preface

I will always remember one late summer morning of 1962. I closed the old rusted, sagging iron gate behind my father's forty or so milk cows. The cows drifted off into the hillside pasture behind our barn, merging with the August fog and totally indifferent to the fact this was my last day as a son of the farm. Later that day I left for college to pursue a different life. I was keenly aware, as I looped the chain around the gate and wood post to secure it, that I was not only shutting the cows in, I was shutting myself out. I never again would enjoy the same intimacy with the farm, the land, the cattle, and the farm community.

It wasn't that I had hoped to be a farmer. I never did like all the endless work, but I loved those first eighteen years of my life just the same. I took pride in my dad's herd of registered Holsteins, in showing heifers at the county and state fairs, and in representing first Green County and then Wisconsin as a member of a 4-H dairy judging team.

But I still felt a sadness that morning watching the cows move out into the dew-soaked grass they would convert to milk destined for the cheese factory a mile away the next morning, when I would be gone. I knew I was saying good-bye to a way of life. Oh, I returned during summer vacations the next three years to continue helping on the farm—milking, doing chores, making hay, hauling oats back to the barn—but it was never the same. It couldn't be. It seems, to enter a new life, an emotional dissociation from the past was prerequisite. I lived most of my life in my home area, but it never was home like the farm was.

After twenty or so years of teaching and seven years after that operating a small business, I once again had the chance to get reacquainted with my farming roots. I began freelance writing as a correspondent for the *Monroe Times*, the main newspaper of my home county, and frequently for *The Wisconsin State Farmer*, a weekly agricultural newspaper published in Waupaca. My feature writing, though never of a highly technical nature, often took me back to farms and, more importantly, farm people.

I might not have always understood their modern operations or farming practices, but I think I could always relate to their feelings about their agricultural pursuits, from rotational grazing on a small, 160-acre farm to a "mega-farm" with 1500 milk cows. Maybe most of all, I could relate to "small farmers" contending with change. Theirs is a struggle to survive, not only economically, but spiritually. They are believers in the family farm and they see the family farm slipping away, much the way I saw my past slip away into that August morning pasture.

Change is inevitable, and I refuse to label it as good or bad, even in the story I have written. I can empathize, though, with the people, who like me, grew up with the family farm as a given, providing a creed in which hard work is rewarded, if not by great financial success, at least by security and happiness. For many these rewards are no longer so attainable, Yet, these people, so attached to their farms, their way of life, hate to give up. For many, there is no other way of life they would know how to live, or care to, for that matter. The one constant among this population, struggling for its very survival, is pride. That, as least, is something that can't be taken away from them.

Writing this story, a tale for children, was my way of once again opening the old sagging rusty gate to walk through an earlier time when farming as a way of life was not quite so threatened as it is today. By no means, however, do I mean my story to be an overly accurate description of the way things once were. Simply, I wanted to open the gate and walk into that pasture myself, getting my shoes and pant legs soaked once again in the summer morning grass. I wanted to, and did, enjoy my walk over the countryside of my past and my youth.

BEYOND THE ENCHANTED BRIDGE:
A VISIT TO SCARECROW LAND

Prologue

The man diligently dug the soil,
Worked it well, sweated in toil.
On the plot of land his garden
He carefully planted and then
Decided he needed something more.
Though it meant another chore
He created there a ragged fellow
To stand guard and wave hello
To travelers on the road close by
And wish them well 'neath God's great sky.

The man, now pleased, stood back and admired
Garden and scarecrow, both love-inspired.
Oh, my, how the green, green garden grew!
And the scarecrow was magic, he just knew.
It never moved or spoke to him, and still
Every time he passed it, a chill
Cooled the summer air. Then one day
When putting his hoes and rakes away
And when his back was turned, he heard
Without doubt, a whispered word.

It was a word without a meaning he knew,
But its power he felt through and through.

There was a joy beyond any known measure,
Richer than the world's greatest treasure.
The scarecrow didn't need to speak any more.
In full, he had thanked his garden creator,
Who, through love, had life freely given,
As good parents will for the sake of their children.

A Surprising Day Begins

Oddly it happened one October Day,
(What day it was I could not say).
It was a day to do nothing in particular,
A day I expected nothing spectacular.
But how could I, a Wisconsin girl—
Big brown eyes and hair in a curl—
Know what was that day in store?
Adventure, mystery, magic and more—
For on this day I traveled far and wide
To a town found deep in the countryside
Where scarecrows dwelt in rustic ways,
Holding dear to precious yesterdays.

Yes, scarecrows, but not those funny fellows
Seen slumping on porches like over-stuffed pillows
When everyone's busy setting the scene
For autumn's drama called Halloween.

No, the scarecrows I met were alive and real,
Walking and talking like it was no big deal.
Each had a personality, like you and me.
Most impressive, their individuality.

I met people made from rags and scraps,
Sticks and straw, twine and straps.
And oddly it all happened one October day
Starting just after breakfast...Oh, by the way,
Before I go on, my name is Martha Marie,
My parents' ten-year-old mystery.
"We don't know where you came from," they tease,
"But feel free to stay, if you please."

They like my brother, too, naturally.
Robbie's only five, the baby of the family.
I'm a fifth grader and nearly grown up.
Robbie, in kindergarten, is just a little pup.
I look after him, being mature and all,
At school I walk with him in the crowded hall
Making sure he gets to class safe and sound,
I hold his hand till there's a teacher around.
At home, Robbie gets away with all kinds of stuff,
But I don't mind. He's just not old enough.
Mom says he's got a mind of his own, and it's true.
We never know what mischief he might find to do.
His sense of adventure just never quits
And it's enough to give Dad and Mom holy fits.
Sometimes he's a big responsibility,
But I love him, tending to him patiently.

In school, we don't see each other as much
And it's a bit sad, the losing touch
With one's sibling so very early in life
Our brother-sister bond cut by a knife.
We are rooms and corridors and floors apart,
But I guess that's all part of getting smart.

Dad once told how his parents both attended
A little country school where they blended
With students of all ages in the same room,
And brothers and sisters could safely assume
They'd be together, within sight, all day,
Working on lessons or during recess at play.
This school, Dad said, had another special feature:
For all thirty kids there was only one teacher.

Students through all eight grades proceeded,
Their progress promoted or sometimes impeded
By the same tireless teacher dedicated
To the idea kids should be well educated.

That's neither here nor there, I suppose,
As far as my strange story goes.
On this particular day we had no school.
Happily, we exclaimed, "Awesome!" and "Cool!"
Robbie said the teachers went to the Army that day.
They were "in-service," he heard Mom say.
Because this "call to duty" came by surprise
She couldn't get a sitter, I surmise.
Thus Robbie and I were left on our own—
"Watch TV. Leave the computer alone.
In the fridge there's the casserole we saved
It's just waiting to be micro-waved."

Mom and Dad worked all day, employees
At a factory turning out tons of cheese.
Mozzarella, Muenster, Brick and Swiss,
Colby, Limburger, Cheddar—a lot of this—

Working in a Cheese Factory

And other kinds too, the best in the world
Coming from milk that's creamy and swirled.
Their hours were long and they came home tired,
I secretly hoped they'd someday get fired.
I wanted them home with me, every single day,
So we could be more of a family that way.

"There are bills to pay," they would explain.
"You like to eat," was a common refrain.
So with quick little kisses and hurried hugs
Our parents were out the door, with thermos jugs
And lunch pails in tow. It was understood,
Naturally, we would stay home and be good.

An Unruly Rocking Horse

I began doing the breakfast dishes
(Admittedly against my wishes)
And to put our plates and cups away,
Perched on a stool that wouldn't stay.
It wobbled and slid as I reached high,
But somehow I managed to get by
Without falling on my face to the floor
While tempting fate in this morning chore.

My little brother, that red-haired Robbie,
Was busy with his favorite hobby
Rocking on his play horse not far away.
On a potentially long and lonely day
He could rock for hours in devilish delight,
Sometimes riding from morning to night.

But today, I sensed, he wasn't content,
His enthusiasm seemed already spent.
He muttered and sputtered many a complaint,
He was hardly acting like a little saint.

He rocked rambunctiously on his horse,
Back and forth with increasing force.
I knew boredom was clearly to blame.
I said, "In a few minutes we can play a game."
He didn't respond but Robbie's racket I heard,
And indulgently offered no scolding word.

I could picture Robbie's antique wooden pony
An heirloom once belonging to lazy Uncle Tony.
Tony is a late lazy uncle, I might add,
And according to Mom, was a shiftless cad.
He didn't amount to much, Dad put in,
Dismissing him with an apologetic grin.
But they insisted we cherish the play horse
Because our grandparents were its source.

These were grandparents from way out East,
Whom we had never met, at least
Not that I knew of—our own relation.
That's what I call childhood deprivation!
Every kid needs a grandpa and grandma, I think.
Otherwise, there's a missing loving link.
Tony the pony came to us special delivery
One day packed in a wooden crate livery.
He showed up with shabby mane and tail,
His front legs mended with rubber band and nail.

Tony the Pony

He lacked any ear at all on his left,
And of beauty, his right ear was bereft.
And even worse—and this was a shocker—
Tony quite literally was "off his rocker."
Mom got out a tube of potent glue,
And Dad clamped Tony together, tight and true.
Dusty and old, our horse still lacked spirit.
We had to do something now to endear it,
So we named it Tony Going No Place
And polished up his old hand-carved face.
So much grime we had never seen before,
But we discovered his handsome demeanor.
More buffing yet revealed character and style—
I guess his beauty had been there all the while.
We soon found under the dust a pretty beast
Made of cherry and leather—a little, at least.

I wondered what kind of horse inspired
The creation of Tony, by what stallion sired.
His eyes were large, luminous, and wild,
The perfect match for this little child.
Clutching the reins draped over its arching neck,
Into the wind of dreams they rode, undaunted, unchecked.

In pursuit of outlaws, perhaps, they sped,
In the long shadows of mountains tall and red,
Across stretches of the wide open West
Among sage and tumbleweed they pressed.
Surely in spirited chase they rode as one
In the exciting land of imagination.

Arabian Stallion

So on my stool I stood, my hands wet,
Soaking in suds, my chore not finished yet,
But the task was really not that bad,
As I listened to the laughing little lad.

Now Robbie was at that age of innocence—
With mundane reality he could easily dispense.
For a moment I thought I could really hear
The creaking of saddle and leather gear.
Then there came a crashing commotion
And I heard Robbie yell with pitched emotion,
"Tony, you're real, you're really real!"
I never heard such a delighted squeal.

That was followed by a clop-clop-clop
And Robbie crying, "Giddy-up, giddy-up!"
What an imagination that little guy had—
His imitation whinny was not all that bad.

I heard the crashing of tumbling down furniture,
And the slam of the front door, I was sure.
His make-believe was getting out of hand
But it was the sudden silence I could not stand.
I jumped from my stool at the sink
(I am a bit short to put away dishes, I think)
And rushed to see what was apace.
Rocking Horse Robbie and Tony Going No Place,
Mysteriously were nowhere to be seen.
I felt awful, if you know what I mean.

Robbie On The Run

Horrified, I pushed my hands through my hair
I saw tipped over table and upside down chair.
On its side the grandfather's clock was knocked,
It lay in silent stillness locked.

Oh, my, I thought, this will cause a rift,
For it was our parents' wedding gift
From the same grandparents aforementioned,
(Proving, I guess, they are well-intentioned).
Like my very heart, the clock had stopped—
For this, I would get properly bopped!
However, I could not worry about the clock yet.
Something more serious waited on my docket.

No pun intended, I faced a daytime nightmare.
I opened the door and looked everywhere,
Up the street, down the street, across our lawn,
But Robbie and his horse were completely gone.

"Could it be," I asked in dismal dismay,
"That Robbie cast some magic spell in play,
Turning Tony Going No Place from a horse of wood
Into a real live horse up to no earthly good?"
I was worried out of my wits, of course.
Just think—Robbie, running away on a great big horse!

"Call 9-1-1," I thought. My parents always told me,
"If anything happens, in any emergency...."
But I couldn't imagine telling the police force
My brother rode off on a rocking horse.

They would laugh and say, "That's quite a story!"
And I would be expected to say I was sorry.

No, I knew immediately that memorable day,
I would have to find Robbie some other way.
If I didn't, Mom would be boiling mad,
And, undoubtedly, so would dear old Dad.
I pinched myself to confirm I was awake,
I wasn't dreaming, make no mistake.

A Man With No Head

It was a Wisconsin fall day, drab and dreary,
When no sun shines warm and cheery.
I grabbed my jacket and a floppy hat
And left house and home in seconds flat.

I set out with precious little time to lose
And scrutinized the front yard for clues.
I found a hoofprint in Mom's flower bed
And then another, near Dad's tool shed.
The prints, though few, left every indication
Robbie had embarked on an equine vacation.
I followed the faint trail to the west
Hoping in my heart this way was best.
Over a few neighbors' lawns I trespassed
But no more clues of any kind amassed.
I reached the highway at the edge of town
And saw a man whose truck was broken down.
He was tinkering with its smoky old engine,
Clanging and banging, he cussed without chagrin.

A Hoofprint

He was a farmer, as best as I could tell
Hauling baled straw, probably to sell.
His truck was old, a vintage model, I think.
With its heavy load it seemed to shrink,
Bales stacked high on this beast of tin.
Its engine sputtered and coughed from within,
As if protesting its burden and refusing
To go an inch farther—it was all quite amusing,
To me anyway—the farmer held a different view.
It wasn't only smoke that turned the air blue.

"Excuse me, Mister Man," I politely said
To the man who had no visible head.
From the road's shoulder where I stood
His head was hidden under the hood.
Moreover, the cloud of dark blue smoke
Totally obliterated any detail of the bloke
From shoulders up. Over his engine he bent,
On mechanical work completely intent.

"Did you see a little boy go by here,
Riding a horse?" I asked with little cheer.

"Yes," said the man, his voice thick as glue.
"Was the saddle perhaps a periwinkle blue?"
(A blue saddle was Dad's brainstorm
While restoring Tony to working form.)

"Yes, yes!" I exclaimed. "Which way did they go?
Oh, please tell me quickly; I've got to know."

"Let's see, it might have been due south,"
Came the words from an invisible mouth.
"Or maybe it was due nearly-north.
Then again, it may have been due back and forth.
With all this smoke about, I didn't see
What direction they took, at least not exactly."

The man never once turned round,
He rummaged in his world of Lost and Found
(Lurking under the propped up hood and stuff)
As if looking for a face that might be good enough
To show a decent girl in such distress.
But he found no face at all is my best guess.

From the back he looked quite odd and quaint
Wearing baggy bib overalls splashed with paint,
His blue work shirt looked oily and wet.
His big ill-fitting barn shoes were funnier yet.
With worn-down heels and turned-up toes
His poor old feet seemed weary with woes.
He looked like no man I had ever met,
He looked like a man who could no older get.

Yet, he seemed familiar, potentially,
As if we were destined to meet, eventually,
Though this was our first meeting ever—
And I just knew he was cunning and clever.

Forgetting I was there, he hummed a tune,
A lonely song that got tiresome soon.

Over and over he intoned his favorite part
(Maybe he didn't know the whole thing by heart).
It must have been his making-some-progress song,
As if to say, "Oh, now I know what's wrong."

"Please, won't you help me?" I beseeched.
So into a pocket he finally reached.
He pulled out some paper, wadded in a mess,
And waved it to me, more or less.
I stepped closer to the mechanical chap
And took from him what appeared to be a map.

The man then said something extraordinary;
"Here's the way. It's both fun and scary.
You will find your brother and his horse
By following this map's imaginary course.
One word of advice I with you shall send:
Always remember, fog is man's best friend."

Never looking up from under the hood,
He added, "I hope your luck will be good."

A Long, Lonely Trek

I stood there puzzled and wanted to know
Which road to take, what paths to follow,
And why he said "fog" instead of "a dog."
Nothing made sense. Perhaps he'd said "frog."
I stood there with my mouth open wide
But my questions stayed utterly silent inside.

Obviously my interview was now terminated,
And so not a minute more I waited.
I said good-bye to the man with no head
He never responded—he hummed instead.

Well, I now had an old map that showed
A mysterious, meandering back-country road.
Studying the map made me even more perplexed.
"You are here," it read at a spot carelessly X-ed.
And in the upper corner in a square, scribbled brown,
A destination was inscribed—it said, "Scarecrow Town."

According to the map, I first had to find
Old Settlement Road but in my mind
No such road existed anywhere handy.
Indeed, this map looked like a dandy.
I walked away from town just the same,
Looking for a sign bearing that name.
I came to a road that was marked County A,
And another, farther on, called County K.
What happened to B through J, I wondered.
Had the official alphabet department blundered?

I passed yet more side roads and junctions,
They suggested diverse and varied functions.
A few lanes curved off to private destinations,
People's farms with colorful designations
Such as Scenic View, Prairie Dairy, or Cedar Vale—
Some reflected success, others were for sale.
Other roads invited travel to small communities
(I thought, "Let one be Scarecrow Town, please!")

Rural Destinations

On I walked but it seemed I would never find
Any road resembling what the man had in mind.
I couldn't believe the mess I was in,
And Robbie, too, to my chagrin.
If I caught up with him, I knew
I would give him a good talking to.
Maybe it wasn't his fault, I granted,
Whatever it was he accidentally chanted.
Suddenly I felt a surge of sympathy,
Or maybe it was my mental telepathy,
Because it seemed I could hear him, distantly,
"Martha, Martha Marie," he called insistently.
His voice, both vague and certain, in the air,
Taunted me with a "Find me if you dare."

His challenge was just what I needed,
But Robbie was being a rascal, I conceded.
I hoped he could tell me with his ESP
Just where Old Settlement Road might be.
Then up ahead, leaning wearily, was a sign
Rusted over time, in a state of decline.
It was nearly hidden from my view,
Nestled in a stand of bachelor buttons blue
And late-season Queen Anne's lace
That in October seemed out of place.

There it was, at last, a little highway
Leading in from the left (if going my way).
"How strange!" I said. It seemed so old,
Yet looked like it had just now unrolled,
Carpet-like, across an open field, the minute before.
Truly, the road waited like an open door,

Welcoming me through a cheerful threshold.
I saw "Settlement" on the sign, then the word "Old."

I felt better now about the map and man too.
With a sigh I whispered a big thank-you,
Though he was miles behind me now, I assumed,
I then turned left where the flowers bloomed.

My journey curved over hills really steep
And down into valleys cold and deep.
But there was no sun in the sky
And dark crooked creeks trickled on by.
They had mysterious destinations in mind,
As if streams could dream dreams most unkind.

All around me in now rather rainy weather
The farmland was the color of old dry leather,
Fields faded by sun and wind and age;
Standing corn, ranks of soldiers in beige.
Regrouping after battle in tattered cluster
Waiting for buglers to call out a muster.
A cold wind blew through their defeated rank
In their desolation my hopes quickly sank.

I met no people, nary a soul, as I strode
On this uphill-downhill endless road.
I passed pastures on sloping hillsides, though,
With herds of cows, their heads held low.
The sight of them, seemingly unconcerned,
Lifted my spirits as I slowly sojourned.
Most cows were black and white, looking dreamy.
Others were colored, bordering on creamy.

Grazing Cattle

A few, here and there, looked reddish brown;
Most were standing, but a few bedded down,
While chewing their cud, they gazed at me,
I think I sensed their curiosity.

I had traveled miles without seeing people,
When suddenly a lovely white church steeple
Off in the misty distance, maybe a mile away,
Peeked through trees, a welcomed display.

The Rustic Trail

Was Scarecrow Town right there in my sight?
I hoped so, crossing my fingers tight.
I soon discovered that my destination
Had not yet made its true presentation.
Truthfully, it was still far away,
And I had a great price yet to pay.

The road I had followed with such resolve
Now seemed to end, to just dissolve.
The map, I guess, didn't lead to any city.
"Well, drat," I said, "that's a downright pity!"

But I was determined to reach the church.
I stumbled ahead with a little lurch
Through a clump of brush and crimson sumacs,
And there, on a gravel path, were Tony's horse tracks.
Eagerly on this path I set out
My heart no longer filled with doubt.

White Church in the Woods

The path opened into a trail nice and wide,
And so I raced on in quickened stride.
The trail, though pleasant, gave me a feeling
It was the path of some historical dealing,
As if Indians and settlers long, long ago
Had walked this way through the rain and the snow
To distant villages for trading their goods,
Pelts for beads, maybe for their livelihoods.
I wondered what they endured, just to survive
And I thought, like me, they were once alive.
It was strange, but it seemed as I walked along
They were with me in spirit, in quiet song
Just a feeling in the leaves and trees,
A slight rustling in the lonely breeze.

I walked and walked and walked some more,
I knew I'd never gone this far before.
Long hours passed. I had left before eight,
But still it didn't seem so terribly late.
I kept plodding but the church so bright
Eventually dimmed and evaded my sight.
Of distant surroundings I saw less and less
As I entered a wonder-filled wilderness.

The brush pushing up against the trail,
Grew dense with its will to prevail.
At long last I entered a tunnel of trees
Casting shadows so cold I thought I would freeze.
"I must be lost," I sadly sighed,
Wondering now why I had ever relied
On the man with the broken-down truck.
It seemed today I was stuck with bad luck.

The Path

A Little Wren's "Sing-Along"

I thought about turning back, but just then
I heard the song of a bird, a small wren,
Nestled in the thicket along the trail.
It sang, "Follow me and you won't fail.
I'll take little jumps from twig to twig;
You can follow in steps bold and big."
Sometimes he sang in words slightly garbled,
While other times he melodically warbled.

I felt cheered by the bird's pretty song
And for a while I followed it along;
It preceded me, the flying thing, flitting
From bush to bush, only briefly sitting.
So glad I was to receive some encouragement,
I didn't think twice about how this bird sent
His message to me in language unknown.
It conveyed its meaning through melodious tone.
Through the tunnel of trees I proceeded
As I did my memory of home receded.
All those things to which I was attached
Now to the distant past were dispatched.

The little wren that I could hardly see
Continued to sing up ahead of me.
His cheerful melody had a glow like gold,
And I realized I was no longer cold.

On the path I saw a hoofprint or two.
I would find those rascal runaways, I knew.

The Little Wren

I followed their trail through the canopy
Shaped overhead by each kind of tree.

Meanwhile the wren darted happily ahead,
Leading me not to the church, but instead
Delivering me to a forest deep and dark,
Full of foreboding, unfriendly, and stark.

Ahead, in the gloom, I saw a small sign,
Nailed to a tree, of a most curious design.
A typical road sign it seemed at first glance
But it wiggled and did a dazzling dance,
Changing size and shape before my eyes,
A sign possessed, I began to surmise.
At first it looked large and perfectly square,
But then elusively elliptical as I got there.
It must have been some sort of magic,
Perhaps portending something dire and tragic.

"Danger Ahead!" read the sign. "Bridge Out."
Then once again the sign changed about.
It now clearly read, "Detour. Local Traffic Only."
"This sign," I said, "is full of baloney."
At such nonsense I had to draw the line,
So I simply ignored the dumb old sign.
I followed the path now curving to my right
And an old railroad bridge came into sight.

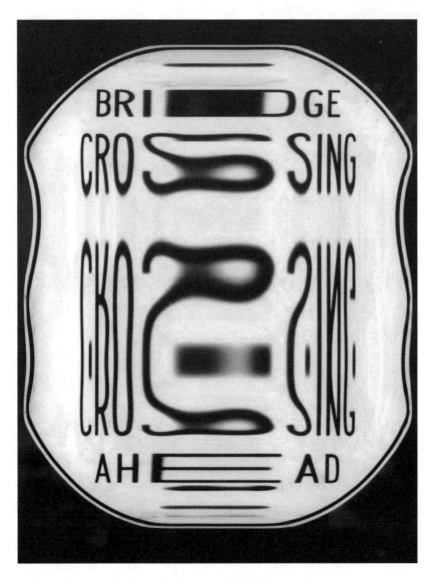

Bridge Ahead

The Enchanted Bridge

The bridge was intriguing, hidden in fog
It was made of wood, not board but log.
With rails removed, no train would come this way,
Unless a ghostly express was scheduled today.
Seeing the bridge made me shudder and shiver
For I knew I was about to cross a river.

Making things worse, it looked very old—
I wondered how much weight it could hold.
About this bridge there was nothing ordinary
And right from the start I found it quite scary.

Instead of going straight, it curved and curved.
This enchanted bridge left me strangely unnerved.
The sudden fog that had come from nowhere,
Settled gloomily over the bridge, chilled the air.
I could not even see, if in fact,
The bridge was out, or if it was intact.
But the headless man had said fog was a friend,
Instead to me it looked like the end.

"If I could see the other side," I said,
"My heart would not be so full of dread."
Beneath the bridge the river rushed by,
Its tormented soul sobbing a cry.
As the river's roar grew loud with despair
A mysterious turbulence pounded the air.
Wicked gusts of wind rushed down the river
Causing the bridge to quake and to quiver.

A Mysterious Turbulence

Before my very eyes it wrung about,
Like a rubber band twisted inside out.

It swung to the left, and then to the right,
Curving its middle in devilish delight.
The wind blew harder yet, in atrocious attack.
The sky went dark, the forest turned black.

The bridge bucked up and turned on its side,
It made me think of some carnival ride.
It pitched and rolled like it must surely break,
It seemed alive, part monster, part snake.

Then all along the jet river bank,
The oppressive air rose cold and dank,
The wind wrestled trees tall and strong
Into shapes bizarre and wrong.
Tortured limbs groaned in agony unknown
And bent down low with sorrowful moan.
Trunks thick and strong strained in the storm
And among them ghoulish figures took form.
Monstrous great faces danced in air,
Distorted eyes at me did stare
Through leaf-shuttered openings overhead,
My heart sank into spreading dread.

Like fingers the smaller branches scratched
At the sky, now with night's darkness matched.
These fiendish figures, like the bridge, seemed liquid,
Their river reflections like ink from a squid.

Tortured Trees

Obviously, I thought, these omens of misery
Meant, "Go no farther, just forget about Robbie."
But that thought was worse than any storm,
To abandon one's brother betrayed the norm.

A Scratchy Voice, A Scary River

Then all grew quiet again, the bridge resuming
Its original appearance, serenely assuming
Its peaceful posture of enchantment in the wood.
I wanted to cross but wasn't sure I could.
The trees stood tall and straight once more
No monsters lurked where they lurked before.
Still, the fog hung heavily in a cloud.
"Are you safe now?" I said to the bridge aloud.

Beyond the fog came a scratchy sound
Interrupting the silence so suddenly profound.
It was a voice, old, rough, and musically impaired.
"Why don't you come across?" it said. "Are you scared?"
Someone was there, on the other side!
"Who's over there?" I anxiously cried.
"I ask once again," said the scratchy voice,
"Are you afraid? You really have no choice!"
There came a laugh, rather sinister and cruel.
Scratchy Voice was treating me like a fool.

"I'm not afraid. I'm no scaredy-cat," I yelled back,
But, to tell the truth, it was courage I lacked.
I wondered who Mr. Scratchy Voice could be.
Was he a nasty spirit that spoke so unpleasantly?

His voice, I thought, had a familiar ring—
Take away its slightly sarcastic sting.

I tried in vain somehow to place it
But soon gave up trying to trace it.
I was too tired from hours of travel
That haunting mystery to now unravel.

"Look here," said I, with determination
My voice full of serious implication.
"I'm crossing this bridge with no end in view.
I'm coming across, unless I fall through."

Again Scratchy Voice laughed—Oh, dear!
How he grated annoyingly on my ear!
"Who are you, you big, obnoxious beast?
Why laugh? It's not funny, not in the least."
No answer came from beyond the fog wall.
I tried to renew communication, call after call.

All was a-hush except the groan of sagging board
But to wait another moment I could not afford.
I took one step, two steps, so far so good.
The bridge held up despite ancient wood.
I never felt so alone as then—
Scratchy Voice was silent, so was the wren.
I stopped and stepped no farther than that,
Instead I tugged down my floppy hat.
With the fog on my face, I became aware
Of sinister sounds coming out of nowhere,

A gasp, a slurp—like words liquid and thick.
These utterances scared me almost sick.
The sluggish river slapping trestles of wood,
Was weirdly pronouncing wet words I understood.

"Murmur, murmur," the gurgling river said.
"Come, Martha, to my muddy, murky riverbed
Where cruel currents rush, where evil eddies swirl—
I invite you in to whirl and spin, little girl.
I hope, my dear, you can swim like a fish
To see you fall in is my fondest wish.

Meet Mr. Whisker Catfish, meet Wicked Walleye.
Play house. Serve tea in clam shell tea cups—oh my,
You can be my darling here forever. Collect treasures—
Angler's lost lures, fish lines, and hooks—such pleasures!
Everyday you can fashion a fancy new dress,
Using odds and ends from my riverbed mess.
For jewelry dangle spinners from your ears,
A broken bobber necklace will adorn you for years.
For music, the Underwater Symphony plays nightly,
A chorus of frogs sings arias unsightly,
Accompanied by violins strung with river grass.
The Bluegill Boys toot tunes with tin can brass.
The final elegance happens to be a heavenly harp,
Strummed by none other than Mrs. Brown-Fin Carp."

Well, these musical delights didn't especially appeal.
To the voice I disdainfully replied, "Big deal!"
More than ever I hated to cross this river,
The bridge's tipsy trestles made me shiver.

Moreover, the image the watery sound created
Left me feeling somewhat nauseated.
"Murmur," said the river, "murmur, murmur.
Murmur, my dear, murmur, murmur."

I shook all over and shamelessly quivered
Hearing the river's message so darkly delivered.
At this moment I wanted to turn and run—
Searching for Robbie wasn't proving much fun.
Robbie! I almost forgot why I was here.
I had to find him and fight off my fear.

The river grew quiet, except for a sloshing sound.
So I gallantly gasped a good-bye to solid ground.

Misty Fog

Tip-toeing, I set out in cautious stride
To cross the bridge with only one side.
Each step was a venture into the unknown,
I was in so much agony. I was so alone.
With each uncertain step, I moaned, "Oh, no!"
But something inside me kept saying, "Go! Go!"

At last I reached the mist-shrouded middle,
To face yet another rip-roaring riddle.
The bridge really did end halfway across!
It was no mirage, or visual loss
Due to heavy fog and low visibility,
The kind that causes spill-ability

On highways, in harbors and airports.
This was worse than those in weather reports
Because the bridge simply ended, Ker-plop.
In front of me in a quite sudden drop.
It was just like someone with a giant saw
Hacked it off. (And that's against the law!)
I got down on my hands and knees to explore,
And groped into fog and found nothing more.

"Oh, this fog!" I thought. "It's thick as smoke."
And just then a woman's soft voice spoke,
"Sometimes, Martha, trust must be blind.
Dare fate to find out what you'll find."

"Who said that? What do you mean?" I inquired.
Of all these puzzles I was getting tired.
"It's just me, Misty Fog. Couldn't you guess?
Let me help you out of this mess."
Misty Fog's voice seemed safe and nice,
But I wondered if I could trust her advice.

She said, "Cross your fingers and close your eyes,
Turn round fast three times full, and, Surprise!"
I thought, "No way! What a dangerous dare!
If I should topple, I'll fall into thin air."

Though of Misty Fog's advice I was skeptical,
I followed her strange instructions one and all.
I was alone, I had no one else to trust,
My options few, I said, "I simply must."

I did as she said and spun 'round dizzily,
Counting aloud, one, two, and three.

"Don't open your eyes yet," said Misty. "Instead,
Without looking, step straight ahead."
"I'll fall!" I implored, wishing I could open my eyes.
"No," said Misty. "Just see what I can improvise!"
So I stepped ahead, expecting to hurl headlong
Into the river—luckily, I was wrong!
Underfoot I felt the warm solid earth.
(Can you imagine what that feeling was worth?)

I slowly opened my eyes to sunlight gloriously bright.
I looked back and there was no fog or bridge in sight.
Happier now, I said aloud, "Thank you, Misty Fog,
And good riddance to you, River and Bridge Rotten-Log."

Exploring A Barn

Ahead of me, dreamlike, was a cheerful countryside
Basking in colors, a wash of sunshine tide.
Leaves on hillside maples had turned red-orange and gold—
Nature was dressed in a dazzling gown, brilliant and bold!
This land was beautiful, peaceful and charming
Obviously its fertile soil was meant for farming,
And yet, the scattered farms were few and far between
Looking neglected, somewhat sad and lean.

I ambled aimlessly awhile, along a feeble fence row
Choked in vines and sumac shimmering a wine-red glow.
Then I noticed an old red barn standing close by
With a silo towering to the hazy high-up sky.

Sumac

A lane, little and lazy, led me toward the farm.
The barn especially possessed a lot of charm.
Inside its mow would be delicious bales of hay,
A horse's snack, tasting of a summer's day.
Here, I would find Robbie and Tony Going No Place
And, with any luck, I could end this senseless chase.

The barn loomed over me big and tall, like a ship
In a barnyard harbor, moored sleepily in its slip.
Two big sliding doors, hanging on hinges, seemed to grin
When I asked if it was all right to go in.
So I said "Thank you, Barn Doors," to be polite,
And asked, "Where do I turn on the light?"

I squeezed through the doors but found no handy switch
Nor dangling string to yank, and the barn dark as pitch.
I couldn't see a thing, but the smell of hay was sweet.
Surely Tony Going No Place would have found this a treat.

My eyes soon to this dark hold began to adjust.
I saw a huge room, covered with cobwebs and dust.
Surely no farmer had been here in years,
But bales of fresh hay stood stacked neatly in tiers.
Shafts of sunlight slanted through dust suspended,
The particles were glowing like a fairy world upended.

And floating around, these myriad fairies dispelled gloom
Revealing the intriguing interior of this gigantic room.
Hand-hewn beams and rafters of hardwood oak
Of ancient carpentry and hard work spoke.

Inviting Barn Doors

Unlike the bridge or river, the barn was silent,
But to ask me in was most certainly its intent.
The haymow was inviting, a playground so fine.
I found a wobbly ladder tied to a beam by twine.
"How exciting!" I said. "I'll climb this spar to the sky
And from the crow's nest see what I can spy."

Up high in the barn, a few pigeons cooed and fluttered
And somewhere bumblebees in an unseen nest muttered
Busily coming and going, and a solitary sparrow
Darted in through a window with slats so narrow.
"What a neat place," I marveled. "Here we could play—
Pirates! Just Robbie and I and our treasure of hay."
Perhaps the barn was listening and cast a spell,
For it seemed just then my "ship" was riding a swell.
Atop a beam I precariously perched, surveying the ocean
And its miles and miles of swaying, queasy motion.

On the suddenly peopled deck below I saw the cabin boy
And shouted, "Tell the good captain, Ship Ahoy!"
Men scurried on the deck while I kept my post,
The other vessel approaching, faintly like a ghost.

"Prepare the cannons," the captain shouted below.
How long I daydreamed like this, I don't know,
But it was time to put such happy thoughts aside—
I had a brother to find, not a ship to ride.
I reminded myself, "Martha, be mature."
And solemnly forgot the ocean's rapture.
I left the barn and said, "Goodbye, Old Doors,"
I left the barn's darkness resting on sagging floors.

Barn Interior

The Garden Scarecrow

To the little lane I returned and noticed
A neglected white board fence all latticed.
It encompassed a spot of green where a garden grew,
But who did the gardening I couldn't construe.
For a good gardener I have a lot of respect,
So I went closer, his horticulture to inspect.

In abundance there were peppers and tomatoes
And sweet corn aplenty in orderly rows.
Off to one side I saw ripening melons,
The vines among weeds, those unwanted felons.
There were onions and garlic, green beans and, by gosh!
Lots of vines full of colorful squash,
I saw strawberries, too, in a pretty patch
And row upon row of red raspberries to match.

It was strangely lonely in that garden so dearly attended,
For somehow life here seemed suspiciously suspended.
"Where are the farmers?" I asked. "And their children?
There should be cows in the pasture and pigs in the pen.
I should hear tractors and machinery in far-off fields,
Combines reaping grain in tremendous yields,
Balers baling loads of alfalfa and golden straw."
But sadly none of these signs of farming I saw.

"All is lost, not just Robbie, but the farmers too.
Oh, I truly wish I knew what to do."

I must have said this out loud—yes, I know I did.
Because a voice said, "You're such a little kid.
How could you possibly resolve—and don't think me rude—
A problem so large, of such adult magnitude?"

Startled, I jumped, then turned quickly around
To determine who, or what, made that sudden sound.
Even more to my surprise, no one was there;
The voice seemed to have come out of thin air.
Of course, after all I had been through,
I now expected anything out of the blue.
It sounded like old Scratchy Voice, in a way.
The voice, coming from somewhere had this to say:
"There are farmers here, once you know of our secret,
I'll tell you later perhaps, but not quite yet."

At first I didn't observe the speaker at all,
But then in a patch of weeds quite tall
Standing not far from me, maybe three feet or four,
Where I noticed nary a soul just moments before,
Appeared a funny figure of curious circumstance,
A man of sorts, fashioned in faded shirt and baggy pants,
And a Green Bay Packers cap; in place of eyes,
A pair of sunglasses completed his disguise.
He had no normal nose or mouth rosy red,
Only a gaping hole in his stuffed cloth head.
A large round circle all stretched out
Formed his horrid mouth and obnoxious snout.

Like French fries in a basket, stems of stiff straw
Stuck out his mouth and jaggedly covered his jaw—

The Garden Scarecrow

Unsightly whiskers in need of a shave!
About his appearance no one could rave.
He leaned lazily against an old fence pole strong and thick.
His right arm reached out, holding onto an upright stick.
A red bandanna dangled freely, waving from his hand.
Though gruesome he looked, I thought he was grand.

And as I stood looking at this man-like creature,
Enjoying each rural and rustic feature,
I hoped that soon a friendship would grow
Between me and this funny-looking scarecrow.
For surely he was a scarecrow, six feet tall,
He had all the traits, he had them all.

"Was it you that just spoke, in such a raspy voice?"
But he answered not, for that was his choice.
His unkempt appearance, so totally intimidating,
Might explain his sorely lacking social rating.

"Hello," I tried again. That seemed a logical greeting,
A safe thing to say when first meeting.
"Could I ask a question or two, or maybe more?
How are you? Are you rich or poor?"
(First, in rules of etiquette, ask about a man's health,
And immediately after, inquire about his wealth!)

Mr. Effigy of Fodder just stood there, looking ahead,
With jagged dry straw and dust in his head.
"Didn't you just say something a minute ago?"
I demanded. "Answer me, sir, yes or no."

Once more the scarecrow didn't speak.
I thought he might be bashful, modest or meek,
But whatever he was, I considered him rude.
I decided to leave, wishing not to intrude.
I turned on my heel to walk away,
But once again he spoke, "Please stay."
Hearing this, I whirled happily around
But again he made no further sound
To indicate in any way he was aware of me.
I was perplexed over this puzzling mystery.

"Very well, then," I announced to his face,
"I am leaving this unfriendly place."
I began down the path, doubting my sanity.
I didn't need help from one so full of vanity.
"You're very impolite, you know," I called back.
"I hope you're happy, you animated haystack!"

A tear or two trickled down my face
As I walked away from this weary place.
I knew I needed his help, as I was lost,
And I had to find Robbie at any cost.
Maybe, I thought, if I acted coolly coy,
I'll still get a word out of this old boy.
And sure enough, my ingenious ploy worked.
On my sympathy's strings he once more jerked.
"Please don't leave me," the voice called out.
"Then talk to me," I answered with a shout.
"There's a limit to my patience, you know.
Either you talk to me or I promise to go."

A Cowboy On The Loose

Indeed, he did speak then, in voice quiet and sad,
"I think you're looking for a little lost lad."
And though he spoke, it was not with ease.
He seemed afflicted with Shy Person's Disease.

Call it inspiration, or just say I was getting wise.
Of course! He didn't want me looking at his eyes.
It might have been a great lack of confidence
That explained his face-to-face diffidence.
So, I stood off at a short distance
And didn't look at him, not even a glance.
I said, "Yes, a little boy on a great big horse,
The two of them romping on a run-away course.

I assume, Sir, you have seen them, then.
Please tell me where they went and when?
Were they in healthy and safe condition?
What was their attitude, their disposition?"

The baggy man rustled, leaning on his staff,
And to my query replied with a dusty laugh.
(I kept my eyes lowered all the while,
And expressed encouragement with my smile.)

"Your brother is fine and dandy, dandy and fine;
He rides sensationally, a cowboy roping sunshine.
His skills in the saddle are second to none,
As good as Bedouins riding in the Sahara sun."

Bedouin or cowboy, this I was happy to hear—
I could imagine him radiantly smiling ear to ear.
Even if nomadic Arab was a leap in imagination
For a character hanging out in such weedy vegetation.

Still looking away, I asked the scarecrow,
"Well, which way did this desert cowboy go?"
"Oh," said Scratchy Voice, "this way and that,
Trotting up every dune and over each expansive flat.
He was riding the range with latitude wide and free
Demonstrating horsemanship with accomplished ability."

I looked askance at the billowy blue sky,
To avoid facing the shy, bashful guy,
"And where might he be now, do you suppose?
Did you notice which direction he chose?"

He said in his corn-husky voice, "I'll be blest!
He first went north and south, then east and west.
Mostly all over, and over all, I just don't know.
He was having fun, so I just let him go."

"Well, that's a fine how-do-you-do," I replied,
For I didn't really think he was justified.
It was rash to let Robbie ride away.
Why didn't he stop him or ask him to stay?

"You're worried," he said, "I understand,
But such things won't get out of hand.
I'm sure your brother won't wander far away,
Not more than a mile or two, anyway.

And I'll help you find him, by and by,
Together we'll round up this small fry.
Please be patient, with yourself and me,
You are young and I'm going on sixty-three.
We have lots of time, all day and more,
Though finding your brother might prove a chore.
Now that you have arrived—safely, I might add—
In Scarecrow Land" (I wasn't sure till then I had)
"There's a fact of which you should be aware,
While you are here, there is no there."

Scarecrow Land Explained

Puzzled, I replied, "That's very confusing."
In silence some seconds I stood musing.

"What I mean," said the scarecrow, addressing my back,
"Our worlds each operate on a different track.
This land, where you are now, has two time zones,
Present and Past, coexisting as twin unknowns.
Once you crossed the enchanted bridge
(And by the way I admire your courage)
You entered the Scarecrow world, the Past,
By fifty years or so, where we at last
Can live again the way we did back then.
Yet, while invisible to you, other men
Farm this land quite modernly, unaware
We often work side by side, each doing our share.
We worked these fields many years before,
And now as scarecrows we do it once more.
We are the shadows at farmers' feet,
We are careful, we are discrete.

Old Barns

We tag along as farmers do their tasks
And listen to the questions anyone asks.
You could say we are their heritage,
The accumulated knowledge of a bygone age,
And occasionally we whisper in their ear
Some advice or encouragement in times so drear,
For as you might or might not know,
Farming in the Present is an uphill go."

I liked this side-by-side notion and thought
How earlier on the trail I had sought
The wisdom of an Indian whose spirit
Might help me if only I would hear it.
Maybe there was someone there all along,
Maybe a chief—who knows—named Autumn Song!

But now I had another guide, one I could see,
And I realized he was still speaking to me.
"Now, one more thing you should know,
Then you don't have to worry so—
Time back home has stopped, just like that,
And will wait for you and that cute floppy hat.
No one will know you are gone for the day—
Enjoy a free vacation, there's no price to pay!"

Intuitively I knew this scarecrow was wise
And I wished I could see his intelligent eyes
Behind those sunglasses so hidden from me;
I imagined them blue and burning intensely.

"Now it's time," he said, "to learn each other's name.
You tell me yours and I'll do the same."

His proposition was polite and seemed right to me,
So I said, "My name, Sir, is Martha Marie."
"It's ever so nice to meet you," he said.
"I'm Buddy, Buddy Blake of Prairie Farmstead."

"A pedigree!" I couldn't help but exclaim,
I approved of such a neat, impressive name.
"I like your name a lot. It has such charm.
Does it mean you own this beautiful farm?"

When there came a pause quite long
I wondered if I had said something wrong.
I kept my eyes down and he spoke again.
His voice sad, he said with trembling chin,
"Yes, but now I'm more or less retired.
My partner of the Present lacks the money required
To farm these few but fertile acres here.
The barn sits empty. The cows are gone, I fear."

"Gee, that's too bad," I replied, avoiding his face.
"This farm looks like such a lovely place.
Now let me see if I've got this right.
If the farmer in the Present loses the fight
Against higher costs and lower prices for his commodity,
His soul-mate Scarecrow also loses. What an oddity!"

Buddy nodded, "Yes, that's it in a nutshell.
If things don't improve, we'll be forced to sell.
Some outfit with a thousand cows will take our place.
And I doubt they'll provide us any space
To carry on with our poor little farm.
Today farming costs a leg and an arm.

These new agrarians come equipped with technology
And, as often as not, a college degree.

For a scarecrow with a herd of thirty head.
I might as well be fodder spread in a shed.
Yet, change is not automatically bad.
Change is change. Sameness is just a fad."
He was sad about happier times gone by,
But to be more cheerful he said he'd try.

A Kind And Generous Host

Buddy, I was learning, had a sensitive quality
And it was easy for him to know all about me.
He knew how I felt even better than I did.
He knew what it felt like to be a kid.
I told him about my day from the start
And he listened knowingly with all his heart.

And, as I suspected, it was Buddy, sure enough,
Who spoke to me at the bridge in a voice so gruff.
That was one thing that I asked him about,
Wondering why he tried to keep me out.

"Oh, that," he said. "It's just my nature.
It's a lot to do with my nomenclature."
"Your what?" I asked. He obviously was bright,
He used big words and seemed, well, erudite.
"My nomenclature," he repeated. "My name —
I'm designed to scare birds. Genetics are to blame."

I laughed, amused, "Maybe you never heard
A girl, unless British, is hardly a bird."
Buddy laughed too, becoming more at ease,
"Do forgive me for frightening you, please."

It was becoming increasingly difficult to converse.
To look away all the time was almost perverse.
"Now that we know each other better," I suggested,
"A face-to-face relationship could be tested?"

"You're right," he said, "how thoughtless indeed.
But please don't stare. It will my speech impede.
I'm rather self-conscious about my appearance—
And I feel a little "hung up" about my awkward stance.
I hurried back here from the bridge, you see,
And re-established my scarecrow identity.
I got all tangled up on this wooden stake
And now can't move, except to shake."

No wonder he looked a mess, I should have known.
He could have been left there for ages all alone,
In merciless manner tied to the stake.
That I found him was a lucky break.
"I'm sadly sorry, I didn't realize your plight.
Helping you down would be a delight."
So I loosened twine and unraveled wire,
And set free the fellow in mismatched attire.
He stretched and kicked and jumped about happily,
And I was happy to see the old chap set free.

A true agrarian, a generous host, and more,
Buddy now looked handsome, not like an eyesore,

Which had been my first, hasty impression.
To see true worth takes more than one session.
A casual glance, superficial and fast,
Results in assumptions that last and last.
In that garden we warmed to each other well,
And a deep trust between us began to dwell.

Buddy noted I had visited the barn already
That he jointly owned with a farmer named Eddie.
Now Buddy wanted to show me his gardening,
He apologized, "It's dry, the soil's hardening,
It needs some rain, and it needs it soon,
The warm, drenching kind we get in June."
I followed him down the various rows
Remarking politely about the varieties he chose,
Though most of all I wanted to get going,
And probably my impatience was showing.

"Oh, silly me," he said as he realized
I didn't care how his garden was fertilized.
"You have more pressing matters on your mind.
To your concerns I mustn't be so blind—
Though I'm really sure Robbie is just fine,
Protected by the Omnipotent Scarecrow Divine."

I had only the slightest idea what he meant,
An allusion to a big scarecrow fairly content
To hover overhead in Heaven all day
Keeping scarecrows like Buddy from going astray.

A Nice, Long Walk

"So," he said, "Are you up for a little walk?
We'll head to town and continue our talk.
We could take my truck, if it would start,
But it's in the garage all taken apart."

"How far away is this town?" I inquired,
The thought of another long trek made me tired.
"Never mind," I sighed, "Let's just hurry up and go."
"We'll get there sooner yet," he said, "by walking slow."

Confused, I questioned his contradiction.
"Here," he gestured all around, "It's like fiction,
Like a storybook land. The slower we ambulate,
The farther we go; and best of all, we're never late.
So, let's not hurry but shuffle for a pace,
Let autumn leisurely lead us to this place."

"Okay," said I, my face brightened by a smile,
And we walked casually on, mile by mile.
We went left foot, right foot, down the dusty road.
Past pastures and prairies, where wildflowers showed
Pleasant faces through tall grasses swaying
As if they were Nature's children playing
Hide and seek, a fun game I must confess
When little I used to play at recess.

Strolling, floating, stepping lightly along,
Stirring up here and there a butterfly throng.

Yellow ones, white ones, monarchs, and viceroys,
And swallowtails too. What grace, what poise!

We drifted over rolling knolls and harmonious hills,
The landscape dotted with barns with rustic frills—
Cupolas, lightning rods, ornate weather vanes,
Rusted roosters, accustomed to winds and rains.

An Old-Time Cheese Factory

We saw, tucked into a hillside, a place
Of some sort offering a friendly face.
It was two tiered, a house and barn combined
Downstairs men worked, upstairs they dined.
No cattle or machinery sat outside
So what this was I couldn't decide.
Buddy was quick to put my mind at ease,
"It's a factory for making cheese.
The kind once most usual around here
Serving just farmers who lived really near.
You might find one every four miles or so,
That way farmers didn't have so far to go."

He explained how farmers trucked milk daily
In eighty-pound cans and took whey home free.
He showed me the window where cans went in
Riding a track with rollers that would spin.
"Gottlieb or Fritz, our cheesemakers so skilled,
Made sure not a drop of the milk was spilled
As they emptied cans into a big tank inside
Where the milk churned in a foamy tide.

The farmers' milk was then weighed
(So later they could be correctly paid)
And then tested for percent of butterfat.
Next the milk was channeled to a copper vat,
And here—now get a load of this—
The milk was destined for wheels of Swiss,
Each one weighing two hundred pounds.
But they weren't as hard to handle as it sounds
Because, you see, they were chuck full of holes.
Otherwise, factory workers, to save their souls,
Would never have lifted them from tanks of brine
Onto cellar shelves to age, like the wild grape wine
The cheesemakers often made, sharing a glass
With patron or customer, a gesture first class."

I found this old-fashioned factory fascinating
And thought my parents would share this rating.

Next, Buddy explained, the farmer drove ahead
And stopped by another window of similar stead.
He pointed to a long narrow track leading out
And running downhill for thirty feet, about.
The farmer here his empty cans retrieved,
And made sure he had them all received.
After that, the farmer had one last stop,
At a cement-based stand with a tank on top.

"That's the whey tower," he said. "See there?"
A long pipe from the factory spanned the air
Carrying whey, a cheese byproduct, to the tank.
And from the tank a hose hung loose and lank

Wheel Swiss

Like an arm swinging from side to side
To fill a barrel the farmer would provide.
Buddy continued, "Nothing goes to waste.
The farmers' hogs get the whey—it suits their taste.
'To slop the hogs' is an expression quite true,
They really slurp up this watery brew."
Buddy obviously enjoyed explaining a process
Done differently now, he said, due to progress.
"Let's go," Buddy said, "Before I begin my spiel
About how I miss those days of the Swiss cheese wheel."

"Okay," I agreed, "but you are the greatest guide,
Especially because of your dairyland pride."
We continued our journey, enjoying the used-to-be,
Unconcerned with the Present, now concealed from me.
Oh, I thought, farm life, it must be neat!
Somewhere a late cutting of alfalfa smelled sweet,
The perfume of paradise in the breeze,
I ended this thought with a sudden sneeze.

I soon saw the Past wasn't a perfect place,
There was plenty of misery on its face.
I saw slipshod sheds and lean-tos ancient,
And weary windmills with sails badly bent.
They moaned overhead, like deposed kings
Robed only in vines and twisting things.
It was lonely there, dozens of farms we passed,
They seem deserted, small plots closely amassed.
"Where are the farmers? The scarecrows, I mean?
Besides you, a single one I haven't seen."

Weary Windmill

Scarecrow Town At Last

"In town," Buddy said, "you'll soon see them all,
Enjoying our festival, held every fall.
Men and women, and children too, of every age —
Scarecrows one and all, borrowed from a page
Of rural life history, free to romp and roam
In this special town they know as home.
On this special day, people leave work behind
And to all worries say, 'Oh, never you mind.'"

I tried to envision the scene, a town bustling —
Rustic folks in overalls and long skirts rustling,
Children, light-footed, scampering around
Hollering and hooting in harmonious sound.
I pictured scarecrow women, their shopping done,
On storefront benches shaded from the sun,
Sitting side by side, catching up on local news —
All the what's, when's, how's, and who's!
Meanwhile, husbands in manner masculine,
Socializing too, over cards at the local inn.

"Just look," said Buddy, waving his hand,
He was beaming with pride for this rural land.
"There's the town where scarecrows dwell.
Listen! They're ringing the old church bell."

As the bell pealed its high noon announcement
Neighborhood dogs howled their own pronouncement.

They voiced disapproval of the deafening bell.
But to scarecrows it was a melodious knell
That meant they would take time out to eat—
It was time to come inside and grab a seat.
To me it certainly was a pleasant sound,
Better than the noon siren back home, I found.
The twelfth gong sauntered through the countryside
Leaving the town strangely silent, as if a tide
Had receded from a sandy beach, with only
One smooth pebble tumbling behind, all lonely.

In the bell's wake, we entered town, as if on cue,
Like actors on a stage under a sky of blue.
A sign, aslant and lazy, introduced "High Street,"
Where cobbled brown bricks wobbled under our feet.
This town was very, very old, I reflected.
Its ancient architecture I curiously inspected.
We ambled past hillside homes stately and tall
While others were modest, quaint and small.
Here and there a tired shed leaned precariously
A horse barn once, and since then, used variously.
In this area, residential and rustic, we delayed
And noticed how the winding streets swayed
As if dancing to Old World tunes only they could hear.
I understood Buddy's pride for his town so dear.

The Cheese Fest

To reach the center of town was our intent.
"Buddy," I asked, "what is this downtown event?"

"We call it the Scarecrow Cheese Fest, my dear.
Honoring our heritage, it's held every year,
On the first Saturday in September, or is it November?
To tell the truth, I don't rightly remember.
When time can stand still for months on end,
I quickly forget what you so easily comprehend."
"This is actually October," I said. "But I'm surprised
This is Saturday, for I was recently apprised
It was Wednesday today when I awoke.
I think you are just making a silly joke."

"Not really," said Buddy, "For you I cheated a bit.
With the week I tinkered to accommodate your visit.
I wanted to have something special for you to see.
Maneuvering through time is my specialty.
Yes, it was Wednesday when you left home today
But I moved the weekend up, so now it's Saturday."

So, Saturday it was, and without further delay,
To find the heart of town, we went our way,
With hope to accomplish the find-Robbie feat.
We turned next to our right, entering Truth Street,
A narrow road indeed, but a good one to take,
For truth is always best, make no mistake.

Down Truth Street a block or two we strolled,
Its decline so steep, we could have rolled
Like empty barrels to the bottom of the hill
To arrive at Cheese Fest in a clumsy spill.
We rounded the last little corner of our journey—
It was like opening a locked door with a key.

Before my very eyes opened a fantastic scene,
The town's center, all astir but still serene.
Scads of scarecrows, short and tall, young and old,
Of toothy smile and happy eye, some shy, some bold,
Freely ambled to and fro on crowded street.
It was a painting of Autumn Harvest in colors replete.
Corn shocks, like Indian tepees, the sidewalks adorned.
Ripe fat pumpkins, orange, round, and bristly horned,
By snapped-off stems, in windows sat displayed.
Variegated gourds, green and cream, were artfully stayed
To streetlight posts ornate by a twist of twine,
And fingers of Indian corn too, the rich red of wine.

I loved this autumn beauty and its successful harvest,
Yet it was the inhabitants here I loved best.
Scarecrows in colorful array—and even disarray,
Women's blouses and skirts fluttering every which way,
Men's overalls, sun-bleached, patch-kneed and worn,
Girls in bonnets and boys in straw hats, all airborne
It would seem, their feet hardly touching ground.
Indeed it was a paradise, a symphony of soft sound.
They seemed so happy, their manner carefree,
With not a worldly worry that I could see.

For Cheese Fest the old town was all decked out
Spiffed up for the day, sparkling all about.
Huge windows on stores winked cheerful promotions
Teasing passersby to purchase old-time notions,
Scented candles, soaps, and beige bouquets,
Or crafted curiosities of bygone days.

And of course the common theme was Cheese,
I guess there was any kind you might please —
Cheddar, Colby, Muenster, Baby Swiss, and Brick,
I saw Mozzarella and snacked on a string cheese stick.
There were too many varieties to enumerate
(Buddy quickly pointed out all were first rate).
"Our main industry here is Scarecrow Cheese,
We can tour the factory, if you please.
A Limburger sandwich would taste so divine.
Or we can hire a mule ride to our Badger Mine
Where early pioneers with black powder and pick
Extracted lead ore underground, rich and thick,
That's how we got our nickname as the Badger State.
This was long ago, of course. No lead of late
Has left our town, and if you're a history pupil,"
Buddy said to me, "It all began with Jesse W. Shull,
Who came here in 1818, establishing the fur trade.
Later with the Van Matre brothers he did an upgrade,
Switching, in 1827, to local lead mining.
By then the fur trade was slowly declining.
The men who worked these mines worked hard,
Burrowing underground with picks, yard by yard.
In the course of this historical phase,
Because of this industrious digging craze
Someone got the bright idea to nickname
The miners as 'badgers,' so that's to blame
For Wisconsin being called the Badger State,
Though mining itself would soon dissipate."

Buddy made Scarecrow Town interesting,
Yet his prolonged history began testing

My patience, as I was increasingly worried.
Perhaps time was waiting but I felt too hurried
For matters historic, however well presented.
Really, it was Robbie's absence I most resented.

"Buddy," I said, "I don't mean to rush you.
I find your tour fabulous, I really do.
But with my brother lost I can't concentrate
On all of the history of this town and state."

Buddy said he understood and with a little blurt
Insisted his scarecrow feelings weren't hurt.
We entered the lower end of the main thoroughfare.
This was Water Street and there was the public square
Graced by a white festive gazebo offering its shelter,
Respite from rain or heat when summers swelter.
Here little children were playing a game, maybe tag,
Cute scarecrows, scampering about in colorful rag.

Just uphill from the gazebo, a block away,
The white church spire watched the children play.
It must have been the one I saw before
Beckoning across the rural landscape floor.
The steeple indicated some secret importance,
Perhaps more than simple happenstance.
It brought me here, in some mysterious way,
There was a purpose, but what, I couldn't say.
I smiled, giving the church one last glance,
Then joined Buddy in our dizzy, downtown dance,
For in this peaceful, special place,
We soon would meet Robbie face to face.

The Singing Veterinarian

We looked for boy and horse, high and low,
Where Robbie disappeared, we didn't know.
"Oh, that boy!" I muttered, "Mama Mia!"
"Come on," said Buddy, "I have an idea.
Hurry up slowly, I know a man nearby
An expert on everything from deer to deer fly."

"A deer fly? Never!" I said in disbelief.
"Now I've heard everything. Good grief!"

Buddy just laughed and kept on walking,
Until we neared a bewhiskered man talking—
Only to himself as far as I could see.
"Uh-oh," I thought. "Another scarecrow oddity."

"Here's our veterinarian," Buddy said, "and his shop,
The kind of place a tired horse might stop."
I glanced hopefully around but didn't see
Any horse tethered in the vet shop vicinity,
An area tacked to the business district's end.
Remotely sat the little office of Buddy's friend.
A sagging shingle read, "Vet Service to the Rescue,"
Advertising the skills of the man now in view.
On the sidewalk he sat, on an upside down pail,
In his lap, a puppy, wagging a fluffy tail.

Both cuddly and cute was this Cocker Spaniel,
And I heard the vet say, "Good dog, Daniel."

The Singing Veterinarian and Daniel

The puppy had floppy ears and big brown eyes.
A paw was bandaged, swollen twice its normal size.
I felt sorry for the poor little creature
(Sympathy for pets is my special feature).
I was about to ask if I could pet the pup
When the vet suddenly with song started up.

"I'm a vet, you bet, a veteran vet.
A better vet, I bet, you've never met.
With knowledge great and college degree,
I know remedies from here to Tennessee.

I overhaul horses that walk with a hobble,
I cure cows that weave with a wobble.
To deal with ornery hogs I have the means
Because I'm a vet who knows his beans.
In my profoundly helpful profession
I diagnose sheep down with depression.
I've cured every cat I've met to date,
Being a vet, I know how to vaccinate.
On puppies I can mend a broken paw.
To my credit I once set a fractured jaw
When two mules got into a stubborn dispute
Over a mare they both thought mighty cute."

Buddy and I smiled as we observed the man
Extolling his virtues, his credo, "I can!"
A true veterinarian, he brimmed with dedication,
Caring was his most effective medication.
He wore rubber boots that came up to his knees
And green coveralls, his armor against disease.

A syringe protruded from one chest pocket
Looking a lot like a kid's toy rocket.
In his other pocket was a medicine vial.
This vet, I thought, definitely had style.

A cloth tag sewn on his left pocket read DVM,
The letters approaching the size of medium.
Around his neck dangled a stethoscope.
Handy was his tool of diagnostic hope.

He peered from funny dot-like eyes
Set wide over a nose of miniature size.
Big black eyebrows, like untrimmed hedges,
Were full and thick, from middles to edges.
His bushy brown beard did luxuriantly grow
Under his chin, he was at least half buffalo.
Most likely he hadn't shaved for years,
For frantic hair forested both head and ears.

I looked at Buddy and he looked at me.
Were we witnessing some sort of comedy?
Of course he assumed a scarecrow's attitude,
So I had to allow a degree of latitude.
Yet we could wait no longer to elicit assistance
So we were explicit, pursuing with insistence.

Doctor Corn Silk

"Doctor Corn Silk," said Buddy. "Please excuse us."
The vet jumped, his eyes wild, his hair in a fuss.

He seemed startled by our direct approach.
His eyes squinted in an expression of reproach.

"Gee, haw!" He demanded, "Why did you sneak up on me?
Can't you see I'm as busy as a vet can be?
This dog needs my attention. Could be infection.
Will he need surgery, or just an injection?"

So we waited patiently a few minutes more
While the man in green continued to explore.
He pushed and prodded the poor pup's paw
Until the source of soreness he finally saw.
A small rosebush thorn he extracted
Doing it carefully as his profession exacted.
With that, Daniel hopped down and limped away,
"Thanks, Doc," his wagging tail seemed to say.

"Dogs love me," said the vet. "I treat them right.
I hope you don't tie your dogs out at night."
I guess he was speaking to us—at last,
His evaluating eyes upon us darkly cast.
He recognized Buddy then and said hello
In a deep voice, rich like that of a cello.
"I'm sorry if I seemed impolite, old pal,
And my apologies to you too, little gal."

I resented his grown-up sexist style
That I was a "little gal," meant only to smile,
Some poor cringing creature in a fairy tale
Who when life gets rough begins to wail.

I was about to put the man in his place,
But Buddy spoke first and I saved face.

"This is Martha," Buddy said, "my newest friend,
She's not little, so let's not pretend
She's helpless, dependent, or insecure.
I think you'll find her kind, honest, and pure.
Today she braved Enchanted Bridge and Mean River
And endured a storm that would make you shiver.
For herself she's quite able to fend,
But now seeks help her broken heart to mend."

The vet looked surprised, then perplexed,
As by a brand-new disease sorely vexed.
He had no ready answer and couldn't say a word.
His stethoscope many heartbeats had heard,
Transmitting a medical Morse code of sorts,
A cardiac message in longs and shorts.
But never before had he been asked to repair,
The heart of a girl, in his words, "pretty and fair."

He fumbled and mumbled and scratched his head,
"This is serious indeed," in earnest he said.
"It could be acute, it could be of consequence.
If you were a horse it would make some sense.
Then I'd say colic from rolling upside down,
But you're not equine," he added with a frown.

"So, it could be old-fashioned heartburn,
But worse, I fear, a cardiovascular concern."
He beckoned me closer for observation,
But I was entertaining a serious reservation

And stepped back from the veterinarian's hand.
He could cure any animal in this land,
But that cold stethoscope against my chest
Seemed a most unwelcome invasive test.
It was unlikely to alleviate my sadness —
The vet's technique was approaching madness.

Noting it wasn't the cure he planned,
Buddy laughed, "No, Doc, you misunderstand.
You can't help her with your stethoscope,
It's more like a case of long lost hope.

She doesn't need your medical remedy,
It's even more serious than that, you see.
Martha's brother is lost and she's terribly sad.
Earlier, a rocking horse absconded with the lad."

The vet took off his cap and scratched his hair.
"Well, doesn't that beat everything, I do declare!
You mean the rocking horse rocked him away?
Oh, this can't be. You talk nonsense, I say.
A rocking horse might inch across the floor,
Turn sideways at best, but to run out the door
He'd require a high-energy breakfast, say,
Of atomic oats, ethanol, and hurricane hay."

"Yes," I agreed, "but it wasn't like that at all.
He had no breakfast, he doesn't even have a stall.
Tony, charmed by chance word, changed his livelihood.
Suddenly right there in the living room stood

What one minute was a toy of lustrous cherry grain,
The next, a big living horse of hairy tail and mane."

Corn Silk nodded a tentative "Yes, I see,"
Then frowned a definite "I disagree."
His body language a negative was displaying.
Instead of hope, his diagnosis was dismaying.

"Well, I'm stumped," he said, "at a loss.
What a happy-go-lucky, high-tailing hoss!
I can't help you, even my college degree
Doesn't help with this impracticality."
He rummaged through some gourds on the ground,
Saying, "I have no medicine for a case so profound."

Buddy said we didn't expect a solution as such,
"We just thought, as a vet, you might be in touch
With someone today who saw Robbie ride by—
A boy on horseback should catch someone's eye."

The poor veterinarian seemed relieved,
For in Scarecrow Land it was widely believed
He possessed a cure for just about anything
His successes numbered in quite a string.
So, my broken heart posed no viable threat—
He retained his title, The Greatest Vet Yet.

We asked again if he had heard mention
Of a boy and horse so out of convention.
The vet said no, he hadn't heard a word.
If someone had seen something so absurd,

The news surely would have arrived by now.
"If it could escape me, I don't know how."

A Bank Robber Out On "Bale"

We thanked the well-meaning vet and said good-bye.
"Well," said Buddy, walking on, "we had to try."
As we sauntered on, it suddenly occurred to me
So far no one noticed I dressed differently,
That I wasn't one of them, a scarecrow, I mean.
I asked Buddy, "Just how am I being seen?
Do I look like a scarecrow? Because no one stares."
"You're nice," Buddy replied, "And that's all anyone cares."
He said no more to explain this situation
And I felt flattered by his short summation.

We stuck to our mission, wearily weaving now,
Through the happy crowd we tried to plow.
We asked about Robbie, but people said no—
For all our efforts we had nothing to show.
Oh, how tedious our interrogations were!
The scarecrows' answers became a noisy blur.
We asked one couple by a corn shock
And of their memories they took stock.
"To see a boy and horse wouldn't amaze me,"
Said the wife, "Because Cheese Fest gets real crazy."
"Truthfully," the husband said, "we don't think so.
But we saw some goats a little while ago."

How exasperating! Goats! Didn't they understand?
Where was that neighborly helping hand?

Many folks we approached on Water Street
And each time we were met by defeat.
They seemed so uncertain, don't ask me why.
They would look at the ground, then the sky.
"We'd hate to say and then be wrong,
Sometimes we're right but not for long.
Maybe later we'll remember, so ask again,"
This they said with an apologetic grin.

I was puzzled by their rustic diffidence
But they meant well, judging by the evidence.
They were sincere, every last one
To a fault—they were just busy having fun.
To me my problems were truly super,
But to them I was just a party pooper.

We threaded through the tapestry of people.
The crowd if seen from high on the steeple
Would have looked like a colorful quilt a-flow
Lying beautifully on the quaint town below.
I only wished I could see the one odd bit,
The patchwork that somehow didn't quite fit,
It might be Robbie a-clop-clopping around,
Then we could catch him and be homeward bound.

We came to a building that looked fairly new,
Modern, looking substantially well-to-do.
"Gee," I said. "It must be a school,
One big enough for an indoor pool."

Buddy chuckled, giving his overalls a yank,
"No, I'm afraid it's our community bank."
As we got closer, guess what we saw!
A bank robber sitting on a bale of straw.
A stout pumpkin-head outlaw with menacing eyes,
He clutched a bag bulging with bills of every size.

He was a cowboy crook with crooked smile,
All decked out in Country Western style—
Red plaid shirt, blue jeans, and yellow hat.
Around his neck, a blue kerchief limply sat.
It had been his hold-up mask, I suppose,
And now was handy for blowing his nose.

His hands were too full of cash to draw a gun,
So we boldly approached him, just for fun.
"Looks like you made a haul, partner," I said,
"What's your alias—Luke, Bart, or Jed?"

To look dangerous the outlaw did his best
And frowned at me like an unwanted guest.
"Look," he growled. "This is my big day.
Why don't you two cowpokes just go away?"

Of this scarecrow bandit I was not afraid.
I planted my feet, and right there stayed.
"Tell me," I said, "Why are you still here?
You've robbed the bank it's very clear.
If you're hiding here by the bank's front door,
Your get-away plan is pathetically poor."

The Bank Robber

Robbie Rides Off Again!

"True," the robber said in a voice not so gruff,
"But robbing this bank has been really tough.
My sidekick, some kid on horseback, proved fickle.
He disappeared and I'm now in a pickle."

"That's my brother, you piece of grime.
He's not cut out for a life of crime!"

I was really upset, you might say furious.
Imagine! Robbie corrupted by a crook so curious!
Yet, strangely enough, I was almost cheerful
To get this news, though it was an earful.
At last we had a confirmed sighting.
Still, I was mad and felt like fighting.

"Don't get your dander up, Suzie Q, dear,
As far as I know, your brother's in the clear.
He didn't like my plan right from the start,
He complied because of his great big heart.
In fact, he tried to change my mind—
It was a rodeo he wanted to find,
Suggesting I could try my questionable luck
Riding wild broncos that snort and buck.
'There's money in that,' your brother said,
'You get straw knocked out of your head,
And I admit a hoof hits like a hammer,
But it's better than landing in the slammer.'"

"But," said I, "you didn't heed his advice,
You robbed the bank, maybe even twice,
Judging by that bag full of loot—
You've even got some stashed in your boot.
Not only that, I see you heisted the vault."
"Clare Bank" said the safe, now his by default.
Obviously he had enjoyed a moment quite greedy
Anticipating a getaway clean and speedy.
But his take was too much for a horse and kid.
What he needed was a forklift and skid.

The robber sat on his bale in abject defeat
Avoiding the gaze of passersby in the street.
"Now I'm really sorry I pulled this caper,
I'll even get my name in the local paper:
'Outlaw nabbed after failed bank attempt.'
Can you imagine this community's contempt?
At least I'm happy for the two-timing kid,
I'm glad he changed his mind when he did."

Buddy, ever so wise, spoke after a moment,
"We're not the law and it's not our intent
In a pistol-packing posse to partake,
But let me a sensible suggestion make.
Take the money inside and say you're sorry.
Tell them you're a farmer in debt, a story
They've heard before and should understand,
It's one told often enough in Scarecrow Land."

Buddy turned to me, "From here to Western ranges,
This is one part of farming that never changes.

Robber, I know your plight and desperation
And jail means a long, lonely separation,
But I also know the Clare bankers are fair.
If you're honest, they'll treat you square."

The robber ruefully said he liked the advice
And would most certainly pay any price
Not to go to jail or bring his family shame —
He worried most about his good family name.

Then we asked about Robbie and how long ago
He had seen him, and so on, you know.
He sighed, "If my memory I can trust,
He rode off that way in a cloud of dust.
That might have been ten minutes back,
But I'm confused, so cut me some slack."

We were hot on his trail, the outlaw said,
"You're not far behind, he's not far ahead."
Though he meant well, his help in this matter
Wasn't much more useful than empty chatter.
So we took leave of this outlaw *extraordinaire*
Without further involvement, call it *laissez-faire*.

We wished the robber the best of luck, of course,
And said we were sorry about Robbie and his horse.
Which of course was not the truth complete,
We were glad he had made a hasty retreat.
I could never go home with such a tale,
My brother, indefinitely detained in jail

For abetting a bank robber in his getaway,
And now must for his complicity dearly pay.
Mom and Dad could never forgive me,
Caring for Robbie was my responsibility.

Cobwebs Most Curious

A few tears had on my face left streaks,
It seemed I hadn't seen Robbie for weeks.
Buddy flopped his arm over my shoulder
And hugged me toward him, a gesture much bolder
Than my dear dad would make in such sorrowful times.
My heavy heart sagged like a bag full of dimes.
For the longest time we strolled the street,
Not quite admitting we had met defeat.
"I'm afraid," I said. "Where can Robbie be?"
This time Buddy was silent. He didn't answer me.

The old storefronts now seemed gloomy and tall,
With blank brick and glass faces non-committal.
They leered darkly, their doors mouthing mock sorrow
They said, "Maybe you'll have better luck tomorrow."
The breeze too, from the few downtown trees,
Seemed standoffish, like loneliness was a disease.
And all the scarecrows just gave a shrug,
Buddy and I alone had our troubles to lug.

We left the main streets behind us,
And entered a side street away from the fuss,
Where no one gave shops badly needed paint.
They far surpassed what is known as quaint.

The area was so different from the rest,
Which had been bright with tidiness blest.

Buddy pointed to one building and said, "Stop,
Let's have a look-see at that small printing shop."
At the old *Scarecrow Crier* office, our outlook bleak,
We saw where the newspaper was printed once a week.

Here, Buddy said, news was in the hands of good editors,
Quite unlike many of today's "media predators."
This paper was always upbeat, no hint of harm,
Just news and a little gossip, friendly and warm.
If it was good, sometimes they printed it twice
And happily sold the second edition half price.

I was so entertained by Buddy's silly talk
I almost tripped over something on the sidewalk.
It was at our feet, there all along, I guess,
What looked like the remains of a mortal mess.
Not unlike a decomposing bowl of fruit, all in a hump,
An unhappy hag squatted there, a human speed bump,
Roundly shaped like rising bread dough,
For the hot oven long overdue, you know.

Apparently she had been there for a while.
She was trapped in sticky cobwebs and did not smile
When we greeted her with a "Good afternoon."
She remained motionless, an unconscious cocoon,
Though this bundle of motionless morbidity
Had no future as a butterfly, in all eternity.
She huddled low, staring straight ahead
From hard hollow eyes black and dead.

Cobweb Cora

Her skin was pale, her whole face furrowed.
Weathered wrinkles and worry permanently burrowed
In the leathery texture of her brow;
Her nose reminded me of the snout of a sow.
If she could utter a sound, I did feel
An "oink" or a grunt or high-pitched squeal
Would have been the most appropriate noise
To come from this soul with so little poise.

Like a refugee bundled against winter's air,
She was wrapped in an afghan needing repair.
A scarf couldn't conceal her hair wanted Breck,
Her stodgy head squatted on a thick stubby neck.
She wore a blue paisley skirt threadbare and thin.
Her knobby knees were pulled close to her chin,
On her spindly legs, white stockings clung
And on her feet black boots loosely hung.

"Oh, dear," I gasped, jumping back a step,
"This peculiar person's lost her pep.
This poor scarecrow, in lowly station
Has lost all power of spontaneous animation."

Robbie Kidnapped

I had never before seen such a sight.
What Buddy said next caused even greater fright.
"I think we've found Robbie," he announced.
"This woman on children has often pounced,
Kidnapping them in a method most bizarre,
Then keeping them like fireflies in a jar.

She's Cobweb Cora, the loneliest woman ever,
And from her victims she's hard to sever.
With sticky web she snatches children,
Who unwisely wander by her now and then.
She probably thought Robbie quite handsome,
Worth more to her than a king's ransom."

"Kidnapped!" I cried. "Taken illegally?"
Said Buddy, "She has done it mentally.
She's evil epitomized, she's very unkind,
And now holds Robbie deep in her mind.
In her lonely despair and aging agony,
She's preyed on both boy and prancing pony.
Through osmosis she feeds her emptiness,
With Robbie's joy she nurtures loneliness."

I gasped, "Does she really have Robbie?
Right inside her head? How can that be?
I know he's not very big but whoever heard
Of someone kept inside a head? My word!"

"I completely agree," Buddy said. "It's weird,
But Cora's mind vastly from normal has veered.
She magically makes children microscopic —
I agree it's a most unbelievable topic.
She absorbs them somehow, through eye or ear,
How she does it is not quite clear."

Cora's toothless mouth was set hard and grim,
Our chances of retrieving Robbie looked very slim.
Buddy said if accused she would deny complicity
And marvel (silently) at our foolish simplicity.

I hoped some other approach might do the trick,
To get Robbie's release, hopefully quick.

In her eyes there wasn't the slightest sign
Of remorse, not the littlest hopeful shine.
The sticky cobwebs held her in tangled knots,
And, brooding, she spawned imprisoning plots
To keep Robbie forever within her self
Like a trophy held high on a mental shelf.

She didn't have a clue about reality,
She lacked any principled practicality.
To hoard Robbie was her ghoulish goal —
To be sole possessor of his youthful soul.
"Yes," Buddy said, "Cora's lonely indeed,
She already has begun on her prize to feed.
She may not look exactly joyous yet,
But inside she's warming up, I bet!"

When he said, "feeding," I was perplexed.
If Cora planned to eat Robbie, I was vexed!
Cannibalism today isn't much in fashion,
Though it was once quite the passion,
In prehistoric times, when my parents were small
And probably painted dinosaurs on a cave wall.

Buddy tried to reassure me, "Though witch she is,
She won't eat Robbie. Heaven forbid, gee whiz!
Let me try this concept to explain —
She's not filling her stomach, just her brain.

She's not hurting Robbie in a physical way,
But a little boy he'll forever stay.
Unfortunately, there are other Coras around,
Though they don't squat there on the ground
Displaying themselves in obvious visibility.
Others can elude us with cunning ability.
Sometimes people, parents, for instance,
Without meaning to, don't give kids a chance
To learn to stand squarely on their own,
Thus they keep them from becoming full-grown.
Such children grow tall and look like an adult,
But a lack of confidence will result."

"Like me," I interjected. "A girl my age
Should certainly have enough courage
To cross the Enchanted Bridge, you'd think—
But my feet and gumption weren't in synch.
I didn't have the courage to continue.
Misty Fog had to tell me what to do."
I guess I was a little disappointed to learn
My courage earlier was perhaps a lucky turn,
That I had not drawn on the "me" inside
But had on other voices conveniently relied.

Buddy saw me struggling with self-doubt
And to put things straight he went about.
"Martha, you are the bravest girl I know,
Self-reliance a-plenty you have to show.
Misty Fog was a case of benevolent intervention,
And that's fine sometimes, but it's my contention

That as you grow older, you need to, more and more,
Draw confidence from your own personal store.
I think today you were very wise indeed
In times of crisis others' advice to heed."

Finally our digression on life began to subside,
While Robbie in Cora's head continued to ride,
Cantering and trotting in her dreamy corrals,
With horse and pale sunset his only pals,
So absorbed in his cowboy debut,
He didn't know he really rode through
A countryside of memory-painted backdrops,
Of Cora scenery, make-believe rock outcrops,
Cardboard cactus silhouetted on sunset skies—
Believing a fake Wild West behind listless eyes.

Too Much Punctuation

We looked at the woman plopped on the sidewalk
And hoped we could get her to talk.
She remained immobile and mute,
As stubborn as a mule you'd like to shoot.

"Hello," I tried. "Look, we can empathize;
We know how you feel, we see it in your eyes."

She showed not the slightest interest.
To her I was an impertinent pest.

Then Buddy said, after pulling me back,
"Let me give the situation a crack.

Would you turn over your prisoner, please;
Such benevolence would put your heart at ease.
Clemency we would graciously grant you,
And no further punitive, penal action pursue."

I was amused at Buddy's diction choice,
Using big words easily in such an easy voice.
The cobweb woman must have understood them, though.
She shifted uneasily, giving her afghan a tug or two,
As if to keep out a cold and weary winter wind.
In her heart she surely knew she had sinned.

All at once, on her lips bubbled some spittle.
Her jowls fluttered, and her jaws so brittle
Began to grind into motion, reluctantly grating,
As if to speak she was carefully debating.

Like a cold car engine, she produced a groan,
And a faint spark of ignition, a promising tone —
We hoped she would speak, and the woman's face
Glimmered a dim light from some inner space.
She opened her mouth, she moved her lips, her eyes
Flickered, headlights flashing lows and highs.

"This lady's ready to roll," I thought. "Oh, speak."
I waited for words but didn't hear a squeak.

"Oh, look!" I whispered, pointing at the air.
Wispy things were ascending an invisible stair.
"What are they?" I asked. "Little space ships?"
And the old woman kept moving her lips.

Buddy said, "They just look like little rows of sparks.
In reality, they are punctuation marks."

I watched the little spits and sputters in flight
Now circling Cora's head in a halo of dizzy delight.
I had some idea what punctuation marks were
And these, so animated, were making a mess of her.
Buddy, to round out my education, felt compelled,
And on the sidewalk a surprise grammar lesson held.

"Punctuation marks are devices for writing sentences,
Paragraphs, or essays. They act like fences
To keep ideas clear or words from going astray.
They are like signs showing the reader his way.
A period means stop, a comma means slow down,
They separate items in a list like 'blue, black, brown.'
Quotation marks appear in pairs, suspended
Over exact words people say—double commas upended."

Buddy made a very good teacher, his subject matter,
Like a delicious meal, served on colorful platter.
In a classroom he would earn lasting respect,
Still on the sidewalk one point I had to inject,
"You just said punctuation marks are for writing,
But this woman is speaking, or at least reciting.
So why would these dots and swirls show up here?
I don't think such things in speech should appear."

"No," he said, "but they are still understood.
To deny their existence does no good.

What happened in the case of our crone
Was this—she became 'overly grammatical prone.'
She grew interested only in correctness
Instead of thoughts and feelings people express.
If someone said, 'he don't', 'you was,' or 'it ain't,'
She dismissed him like an empty can of paint."

"It's what people mean, not how they say it,"
I agreed, "It's the tune, not how they play it."

"Well put," said Buddy, "Yet savor the thrills
You can attain with good language skills.
If you speak well, or write well, people notice
And distinguish you from the unstudied novice,

Not that Cora isn't studied—she really is.
She taught English and was quite a whiz.
But being a critic cost her many a friend,
It's left her lonely and speechless in the end.
Her mouth conveys no words, just structure and form,
And mostly punctuation, which comes in a storm."

It was true. Commas and semicolons and parentheses
Swarmed about, as meaningless to us as Swahili or Chinese.
"You mean, all these cobwebs, all this clutter,
Is punctuation, the only thing she can utter?"

"Exactly," said Buddy. "Nothing but grammar dust,
She's caught in a habit she cannot bust.
Preoccupation with words delivered without flaw
Turned her so cold, I doubt she'll ever thaw."

The old woman kept moving her mouth all about
And more unheard words kept coming out.
Her efforts to speak were a work of intensity
But she remained a mystery of darkest density.
She spewed out periods, commas, dots unending,
Like spirals of ribbon unraveling and bending.

I looked at Buddy, my hands imploring.
"Oh, Buddy, what can we do? After all our exploring,
We've reached this impasse, an impossible juncture,
It's like our last tire has suffered a puncture."

Buddy's Friend Pat

A dim light on Buddy's face began to show,
At first a glimmer, then a gleaming glow.
"I know just the scarecrow to help us!"
He jumped up and down and made such a fuss
He caused bits of straw to scatter—
Even Cora's teeth began to chatter.
Huddled there, in her tomblike trance,
She sensed something was up, from Buddy's dance.

"What's on your mind?" I quizzically queried,
But Buddy grabbed my hand and we no longer tarried.
We raced down the street, as slowly as possible,
Leaving old Cora behind, mean and miserable.
"It's this way," Buddy yelled, "Let's hurry."
So we shuffled, our pace hardly a scurry.
We dragged our feet and quite frankly appeared
Like Sunday drivers who hardly ever steered

As they casually toured countryside inviting,
Leaving others in a state of fingernail biting.

We inched downhill, hanging left on Water Street,
And at a breathless crawl we tried to compete
To see who could come in last and still be first.
Believe me, we didn't work up a burning thirst.
But Buddy's theory that slow motion was fast
Was a notion that I got in my noggin at last.
It was an ironic race, its main feature
To come in last, behind this lovable creature.

We didn't go far, or couldn't, at this pace
Before stopping in front of a most beautiful place.
"This is Pat's house," Buddy said, "A grand affair,
A mansion with an antebellum Southern air."
All around, a beautiful melody seemed to sing.
The home was elegant, a castle fit for queen or king.
Surrounded by roses denoting royal privilege,
All that lacked were turrets, moat and drawbridge.
From real estate so aristocratic I ruefully expected
Any plea for help would be regally rejected.

"There she is," Buddy said, "taking a needed break."
I saw a woman resting, leaning on a garden rake,
A black little bird, a miniature crow,
Perched on her shoulder, wouldn't you know!

Pat was dressed for work, I think—
A baggy plaid shirt blue and pink,
And faded jeans held up by baling twine.
This looked silly but served the purpose fine.

Pat and Crow

"Pat!" Buddy cried out, flapping arms wildly.
His exuberance embarrassed me, but only mildly.

Pat looked up and did a double take.
"Goodness' sake!" she said, dropping her rake.
To her bird she said, "Would you look at that!"
The woman waved back with her old straw hat.
The crow with his wee wings flapped the air,
Luckily doing no harm to Pat's auburn hair.

Buddy and Pat, like long lost friends
To whom Fate sometimes a second chance sends
To patch up a disrupted good thing,
Stretched their arms out, as if to sing
An operatic aria in a moment climactic
Bringing to end a drama otherwise tragic—
I wished it were the one involving my brother!
They raced (slowly) toward each other,
Buddy bumbled toward her and she toward him
Like two silly kids goofing off in gym.
They embraced in joyous juvenile burst,
While I lagged behind, standoffish at first.
The two scarecrows hopped and hugged so hard
Straw of ecstasy exploded across the yard.
Fortunately they regained self-control quickly—
Their contents were covering the lawn thickly!

Sanity had returned to this happy scene
Of wondrous reunion I had come between.
Pat proved unpretentious, genuinely warm,
She was wonderful, full of big-hearted charm.

Her eyes danced in delight, her voice was kind,
A nicer woman it would be hard to find.

"What's your bird's name?" I finally asked Pat.
"He's so cute in his red scarf and little hat."
"Oh," she said, "I don't rightly know.
I just call him 'The Refuse-to-Grow Crow.'"

For a crow he was small, I had to admit,
All the more reason the name seemed to fit.
Out of proportion grew his yellow beak
And later I would learn he could even speak.

As in any reunion after long separation
A clumsy silence suddenly needed reparation.
I stood speechless, Buddy hemmed and hawed,
But this frozen conversation Pat quickly thawed.

"What do you think of my flowers, Buddy?"
So he stepped back to do a farmer's study
Of Pat's flowers so blessed with bloom.
"You like my mums the best, I assume."

Of these pink bouquets she was proud
And didn't mind saying so, right out loud.
Yet with modesty she acknowledged implicitly
The credit belonged to Nature's simplicity.

"Oh, the mums," said Buddy, "truly are magnificent.
Because just like you, they're heaven sent."
Two pink spots of blush appeared on Pat's cheeks
And Crow uttered several self-conscious squeaks.

"I meant every word," Buddy said, "I really did.
Now about another matter I must be equally candid.
We've come here to ask a favor, not to visit.
I fear we don't even have time to sit.

You see, Martha's little brother, we truly dread,
Is trapped in the Cobweb Woman's lonely head.
He's riding a spunky horse of wayward pace,
Roaming the deep darkness of her mental space.
We hoped you, and Crow, might help get him free
And put an end to my friend Martha's misery."

The Special Brew

I knew a happy outcome was not for sure,
And Pat's beautiful yard became a wet blur.
I turned away, trying to hide my tears,
I was embarrassed, a girl of ten whole years.

Pat gently pulled me to her flannel shirt,
In her straw bosom I buried my fear and hurt.
Here I felt so warm and comfortable
My problems didn't seem so insurmountable.

"So," said Pat, letting Buddy's words sink in,
"It sounds like Cora's up to mischief again.
That tiresome woman!" She uttered with a groan.
"It seems we can never leave her on her own.

No indeed," she continued. "This will never do.
Crow and I will have to cook up a special brew.

We shall employ our secret scarecrow magic
And undo Cora's deed so potentially tragic."
Her mood turned almost merry, even silly.
"I've learned all the tricks of this land so hilly.
You might say I know all the ups and downs,
I know exactly how to extract smiles from frowns.
We'll fix her wagon," she chirped, "Yes-sir-ee,
We'll concoct a frothy frost to end Cora's misery.
Now, you know what to do, Refuse-to-Grow Crow,
Flutter your wings, feathered friend, hurry, go."

Like a little tornado, Crow spun in the air
Then flew dizzily, first here, then there—
Around the yard, among the flowers, in the trees,
Dipping and diving in the fall day breeze.

I was impressed. The bird was cunning and cute.
Buddy thought so too, saying, "He's a hoot."
Pat then began gathering sticks, as dry as dust.
"Let's see," she mused aloud. "A fire is a must."
From somewhere she produced a big black pot
And into it poured water, but not a lot.

"Next we'll need something for Cora's cure,
Something sweet, loving, gentle, and pure,
Like my mums, my roses, at least a petal or two,
And pages from good books like *Winnie-the-Pooh*.
We need to reach her deep in the heart—
That's where good communication must start.
It may seem a shame to cook a book
But we need to give Cora a brand new look.

The pages will melt but the words will stay,
To enter that woman now turned nearly to clay."

Pat dropped book after book into the pot,
Books I had read and loved and loved a lot.
I just hoped she knew what she was doing,
I just hoped she knew what she was brewing.
Pat reached into her shirt pocket for a match
And against her rake handle gave it a scratch.

Meanwhile, Crow, with his inventive brain
Gathered a bird song with the sweetest refrain,
Perhaps that of an oriole with a nest overhead,
Or of a meadowlark on a fence post instead.
How he caught the melody and held it perfectly
Will always to me remain a musical mystery.

Crow made many trips, flight after flight,
Each time returning with a different delight.
Nature, I already knew, offered many pleasures
But crow kept discovering amazing treasures—
Reds and golds from autumn trees that dream,
Shimmering light from a rippling stream.
Magically he managed to catch perfumes
Of flowers, of forest floors, of quiet rooms
On a sunny afternoon when folks often rested
Or visited, softly, in pleasant voices vested.

Pat's cast iron pot began quickly to fill
It was so full I was afraid it would spill.

Whatever she was making, it smelled delicious,
Almost too good for a woman so malicious.

Final Preparations

Pat seemed pleased as she stirred the brew.
"I think it's done. There's only one thing left to do.
Come on, everyone. To the whetstone we'll go
We'll transform Crow into a needle-nosed dynamo."
Pat led the way with Crow fluttering overhead,
And we followed, stepping around a flowerbed.
Around the house, minds intent on devious plot,
We headed, straight to Pat's arbor, a shady spot.
Supported on four wobbly legs of wood before us
Was a big stone wheel that moaned a whirring chorus
As Buddy cranked the handle, slowly at first,
Then ever faster, till the shaky frame nearly burst!

"That's it!" exclaimed Pat with an appreciative eye,
As she trickled water on the whetstone dry.
Then Crow hovered close and pressed his beak
To the turning stone, resulting in a squeak.
Sparks flew off the wheel in a shower—
Luckily this took only a minute, not an hour.
Once his beak was sharp, Crow took to the air
Flying around to show off how dapper and debonair
He looked, sunlight shining from his sharpened beak.
His confidence was contagious in a time so bleak.
Headlong he sliced through the autumn breeze,
He pleaded, "Turn on the garden hose, please,

Sprinkle a fine fan-shaped mist against the sun,
And I'll show you how laser surgery is done."

Buddy hooked up the hose, handy and ready,
And happily produced a spray, misty but steady.
Near the tops of Pat's ornamental lawn trees
The water spread out one hundred eighty degrees.
A bright shaft of sun then agreed to bestow
In plain view an iridescent, radiant rainbow.

At this ribbon of misty color, Crow took a run,
Hurling headlong into its hues and having fun.
He first sliced red from orange, then orange from yellow,
He then attended to green like a greedy fellow.

Once green was pared off by his scalpel beak
He set upon blue, and then the indigo streak.
Only a violet bridge remained now in the sky,
And on this he perched with a smile quite sly.

Crow clutched the remaining arc with his toes.
Laughing, we forgot our sorrowful woes.
Then Pat brought us back to the here and now.
"It's time," she said, "to hitch horse to plow,
While the sun shines, let's make our hay.
I can't wait to put this plan in play."

Crow swooped down with a squawk and flutter,
He dived smoothly, like a hot knife through butter.
"Let's," he cawed, "loosen her pesky punctuation.
Let's," he jawed, "free Cora from her joyless vocation."

"To the cauldron, then," said Pat, leading the way,
"Before our secret soup has boiled away."
As we retraced our steps to the front yard fire,
Pat told how Cora was once a person to admire.

"I remember her when she was a youthful soul
When her mind and heart both were whole.
She was happier then, as I recall, and pleasant too,
But she always was shy, even more than you."
(This she addressed to me, I guess,
But she said it with the utmost kindness.)

"Cora was in love once upon a time,
When she was pretty and in her prime.
She was engaged and a wedding date was set
But the man backed out without the least regret.
This broke her heart—the poor scarecrow.
Even a heart of straw breaks, you know.

Sadly she avoided all fun and society
And retreated into a world of verbal propriety.
Here she felt safe and sure of herself,
Trusting only the books on her shelf.
And, these books, to make matters worse,
Dealt with rules of grammar, outdated and terse.
She should have read something more lighthearted,
Something that would have some joy re-started.
But I know, somewhere deep, Cora has a soul
And could be happy, if made healthy and whole.
If all goes well, if Crow can do it right,
We might restore Cora to a disposition bright.

You'll see how the magic we have in store
Will get Robbie back and perhaps do much more."

Potion In Motion

Pat fumbled through garden tools in a pile,
At last her face lit up with a smile.
She held up a device like a big tin can
Hung under a hand-held pump labeled "Bug Ban."

She called it "Rusty," this insect-sprayer,
And wished for luck in whispered prayer.
"This will work," Pat explained, "as our atomizer,
Once we fill it with our brewing tranquilizer."
Using a funnel, the oversized tin can she filled
With our syrupy brew, and not a drop was spilled.

Just once, downwind from us, she pumped the device,
And out came a cloud of stars sparkling like ice.
The twinkling mist settled slowly to the ground
And suddenly thick frost covered everything around.
Every blade of grass and every little flower turned white
And glistened like a winter's day, pure and bright.

"Cool!" said I, filled with amazement surpassing awe.
"How long does it take this tundra plot to thaw?"
"Oh, not long," said Pat, "perhaps a minute, not much more,
And then the flowers and grass will themselves restore.
Better yet, the blossoms will be brighter, the grass greener.
In fact, everything around will have a happier demeanor."

I began to see what she had in mind for Cora too,
This potion would give the woman a real redo.
We crossed the expansive lawn delightfully,
Two scarecrows, a happy bird overhead, and me!
We reached the sidewalk and walked up the block,
Intending with Cora our figurative horns to lock.
On the sidewalks, scarecrows stopped and stared
Puzzled at our purposeful parade but no one dared
Laugh aloud, or ask what we were thinking about—
They could see we meant business, I have no doubt.

My heart was beating fast, the excitement growing,
And I felt a bit of panic set in, knowing
Robbie was in such an insane situation—
From Cora's employment he needed a vacation.

Without thinking, I began to walk faster
But Buddy reminded me, kindly like a pastor,
To just take it easy, or my shoes would smoke.
How gently he reprimanded me—with a joke!

Along we hurried, like snails side by side,
Until up ahead Cobweb Cora we spied,
Where we left her before, a big bump on the sidewalk
In her web of punctuation and silent talk.

Crow flew ahead and, brimming with emotion,
Fluttered over Cora's head, making a commotion.
Pat and the rest of us caught up to Crow
And next to Cora stood toe to toe.

At first Cora took no notice of our arrival,
It was Pat who said to our rebellious rival,
"So, you old rascal, with your silence unending,
It seems once more your manners need mending."

Cora shifted her gaze of molten lead
To look up sheepishly toward Pat's head,
But otherwise did not stir, quite unmoved.
She seemed used to being harshly reproved.

"That does it," said Pat. "Stand clear!"
We jumped back, mostly out of fear
We'd all be sudden icicles by accident—
We knew exactly what Pat's warning meant.
She pointed trusty Rusty and took careful aim,
Pumping a dose of magic mist at the dusty dame.
In the blink of an eye, Cora turned paler than gray,
And then white—and ice white she did stay.
Cora's cobwebs grew thick with hoary frost,
They drooped and sagged and finally lost
Their sticky hold on her, that haggard mess
For whom I now felt rather sorry, I confess.

She shivered as the frost penetrated deeper,
And Pat said, "There, that ought to keep her.
Crow, get ready for your all-important assignment.
Check wind speed, vector angles, and beak alignment."

What happened next, I'll never forget.
Crow backed up from his iced-over target

Refusing to Talk

And while hovering at a standstill mid-air
Beat his wings faster and faster, to prepare
His precipitous and dazzling descent
Into a woman who now was hard as cement.
As he whirred his wings before our very eyes,
He shrank and shrank to an ever-smaller size.

With a burring buzz like a dentist's drill
He was ready his mission to fulfill.
Like a jet aboard a ship, engines whining,
He was the work of advanced designing.
So tiny he now appeared—a mere dot—
He was still diminishing, right on the spot.

"Okay, Crow," Pat said. "That's small enough,
Now dive, you devil, and do your stuff."

Buddy and I were merely there to "spectate,"
But Cora would get a taste of crow-concentrate.
Nearly invisible, Crow aimed at Cora's forehead—
A needle straight and true, his path a tiny thread.
He shot for a wrinkle that looked just right
And suddenly Crow disappeared from sight.

"Oh, ouch!" I said, "Crow's entering her head."
"Indeed he is," Pat reassuringly said,
"But don't worry, she's so numb and cold,
She won't feel a thing, unless she is told
What we did here in sidewalk surgery,
So let's all swear to an Oath of Perjury."

It was a paradox, not to tell the truth,
Something I had been taught in my youth.
But Pat proceeded and we held up a hand
And listened on our sidewalk witness stand.
"Lies and only lies we promise to tell,
We'll never disclose the magic spell
Or how we concocted our magic mist,
On these sacred secrets we must insist.
Note the fine print: accidental blabbing
Will be perceived as blatant back-stabbing."

Like in a huddle during a game, sometimes before,
We put our hands together and solemnly swore.
I felt kind of foolish but didn't really mind
Swearing loyalty to folks helpful and kind.

Moments had passed and Crow was still in there,
Buzzing around beneath Cora's mat of dingy hair
Deep in the world of her uncharted brain
Where Robbie explored, giving Tony free rein.
Cora I noticed was apparently still asleep,
Dreaming, for on her face with its furrows deep
Signs of disturbed emotions seemed to surface—
A puzzled frown, a sneer, once a grimace.
Something was happening in that dim desolation,
For we all witnessed a gradual transformation.
The old leathery face I saw before
Was now soft, pliant and, what's even more,
It started to look pleasant, after a while.
Yes, the old lady slowly began to smile.

Cora's Glacial Facial

"I believe," said Buddy, "these signs indicate
We got here not a minute too late.
Martha, this day will end happily,
All from following that map, you see.
Meaningless as it seemed, so greasy and old,
You took charge; your instincts took hold.
An X in a territory unknown to you
Is now a reality you have lived through."

I had forgotten all about the map,
The stalled truck and the unlucky chap
Who all the while had hidden his face—
"So, it was you who sent me to this place!
You are a rascal! Everywhere you appear.
It was you all along that brought me here."

"No, Martha, you brought yourself, all the way.
I just nudged you a bit, you might say.
Anyway, I thought by now," he said, "you knew."
Just then the sky turned a terrible black-blue,
A wind, ferocious and hot, howled high overhead,
Lightning flashed fire from clouds like lead.
From the heavens a horrible madness rumbled,
And helplessly onto the sidewalk we tumbled.
All of us (Cora as well) ended in a pile—
And Crow too, like he'd been there all the while.

The spell had worked, with heavenly intervention,
But I didn't know it was Pat's intention

To stir up a storm that would shake us so
But this time I guess she really let it go!

The sky grew bright once more, the wind died down,
A sense of well-being returned to Scarecrow Town.
Buddy stood first, readjusting his sunglasses,
As if preparing to speak before the masses,
And next helped Pat and me from the sidewalk,
So roughly shaken we could barely talk.

We all inspected ourselves, regained composure,
And counted ears and noses, just to be sure.
Luckily, no great amount of straw was lost,
Considering how the scarecrows had been tossed.

Cora too, now stirred to her feet, no worse for wear,
In fact the wind had done wonders for her hair—
She was vastly improved, no cobwebs or dust in sight—
Her eyes sparkled with a sensational new light.

"I see," said big-again Crow, "you are dazed,
But when the air clears, you will be amazed.
Let the great scarecrow surgeon of spirit
Receive your praise. Come on, gang, let's hear it."

What was wrong with this egotistical bird?
Had he gone mad in the melee, we wondered.
Then we knew just what he meant—
There sat Robbie on his horse, smugly content.
Tony Going No Place pranced, nodded, and neighed,
And Robbie boyishly a happy smile displayed.

He climbed down from his high-mount horse
And hugged me long with fantastic force,
Happy tears sparkled in his eyes, and in mine—
We were filled with feelings difficult to define.

Our happiness, so hard to conceal, was contagious
And all of us became slightly outrageous.
Pat and Buddy hugged each other blue,
And Crow in crazy circles over them flew.
(I suspected there might be a wedding,
Down the path those two seemed to be heading.)
Cora stretched her arms, yawned and sneezed,
No cobwebs, at last! She was ever so pleased!
After countless years, she finally spoke—in sound.
Her voice she had joyously once more found.
No commas, quotation marks, or punctuation at all,
Only music from her lips did sweetly fall.
"Oh thank you very much," she sang in soprano.
"You have set me free," she sighed in soft piano.
"Oh, dear! What misery! What damage have I done?
I bet I've been a fool, a real son of a gun.
My perspective on life got twisted around.
Thanks to you, my feet are back on solid ground."

We gave her an update but kept it brief
On her misdeed with Robbie—and my grief.
Big wet tears spilled from her eyes,
Her sorrow she could not disguise.
"I love children. I can't imagine why
Little Robbie's freedom I ever would deny.

Forgive me, if you can find it in your heart,
And from this day on I'll make a fresh start."

We forgave Cora, of course, and hugged her too.
It's just great what a little love can do.
We simply told her love could not be demanded,
It couldn't be earned by means underhanded.
She now understood she could not take
Something most of us give freely, in goodness' sake.
To show our sincerity, we hugged her once more,
And poor Cora—her tears really began to pour.
Her face was wet but really lovely—it beamed.
"I'm happier than I ever would have dreamed,"
She said, helping herself to another squeeze.
"Oops," she said, "I should have asked, 'Please.'"
We laughed, "Oh, Cora, that hug wasn't demanded,"
And we hugged again, while Crow lightly landed
On her dear old head and cawed raucous approval,
For it was his little piece of memory removal
That had made her happy and at the same time
Certainly saved little Robbie, whose greatest crime
Wasn't bank robbery after all but trusting too much
In those who really are strangers, as such.

Farewell To Scarecrow Town

Robbie was safe again, bursting with joy—
What a day he'd had, this little cowboy!
Later he would have endless stories to tell,
I could see it in his eyes, deep as a well.

But our time in Scarecrow Town was about to end,
Day's shadows, now long, with dusk began to blend.

"Come on," said Pat, "the day's getting late.
The sun's headed for its western gate.
As much as I hate to see you on your way,
It's time to head home, unless you plan to stay."

"Could we?" Robbie said. "That would be great!
There's this bank robber I told to wait."
This thought changed everything—I saw it in his face.
He now had second thoughts about this place.

I mustered my best mom-imitation voice and said,
"Your robber friend, Robbie, was shot full of lead."
Robbie's eyes grew wide as he realized
An outlaw's fate is often romanticized.
"It was," I said, "a foolish undertaking, you see,
Even to consider such a law-breaking spree."
Buddy chuckled and said I was being naughty.
"Well," I said, "that's the way my parents taught me."
"You kids are such delights," said Pat,
And Cora chirped in, "They are at that!"
"It would be nice if you could stay," Pat conceded,
"But go home where we all know you're needed—
Your folks love you, more than you know.
Always believe this, even when it doesn't show."

Farewells are sadly necessary, of course.
So Buddy helped us up on Robbie's horse.

"I'll walk you to the village edge, my friends,
And to the path that magically sends
Travel-weary children home, safe and sound,
So far away from this special land you've found.
Don't look back, don't cry, and don't be sad,
Just remember the good time you have had."

We waved good-bye to Pat and Crow and Cora too,
Turned quietly, leaving them without any ado.
Buddy led Tony by his bridle through the street,
Stopping only once to get us one last treat,
Tasty cheese curds deep fried and hot.
We were starved and they really hit the spot!

We went a little farther, the festive crowd thinning.
I spotted a familiar face or two, each winning
Our final appreciation and a good-bye wave—
Each face in our memories we would save.
The would-be robber was talking to the banker
Who seemed good-natured, not full of rancor.
Though the bandit still awaited his final fate,
He yelled, "Don't worry, Robbie. I'm glad you were late!"

The veterinarian too was still doing his best
Ridding every animal of disease or pest.
Daniel the puppy was back in his lap
And talked back to the vet with a yap.
We clip-clopped up the hill to Truth Street,
Buddy silently walking a solemn retreat
And once more, six times, the church bell chimed.
Finally to the town's outer limits we climbed.

"Here's the path to take," Buddy said,
Pointing off in a general direction ahead.
"There's no trail or road of any kind.
But the way home your horse can easily find."

We said our final good-bye and I was really sad,
I told Buddy, "You are the best friend I ever had."
Robbie tried to say something appropriate too —
Squeezed behind me in the saddle periwinkle blue.

"Buddy," I said, "Do you think, do you suppose,
We could ever see each other again, if we chose?"
I was awkward, like a girl on her first date,
But I had to know if it would be our fate
To enjoy each other's company again. Tragic
It would be not to ever again know the magic
Of talking with Buddy, walking hand in hand
Through his wonderful, beloved Scarecrow Land.

Curiously, he said just this, "You never know.
Nothing is impossible for a scarecrow."
With that he gave Tony a gentle slap.
We were on our way, now without any map.
I looked back, "Oh, Buddy, I am so blue,"
But Buddy was gone, and the town was too.

A Sleepy Ride Home

Me being bigger, I rode in front of Robbie
And he wrapped his little arms around me.

It felt so good to have him safely found—
It felt even better to be homeward bound.
I only hoped what Buddy said was true,
About time standing still, or what a stew
We'd be in when we arrived late at night,
With the front room left in such a sight.

The sun was setting with a rosy warm glow
As we traversed a pleasant, aromatic meadow.
Sometimes we'd see a farm way off somewhere,
Isolated and lonely, and in the evening air
We could hear the moos of cows at milking time
Or the barking of a dog in pleasure sublime,
Herding the cows to pasture for the night.
Above, myriad stars provided a dazzling light.

A full October moon, orange and dreamy,
Turned the landscape all soft and creamy.
Rows of corn shocks in one hillside field
Slumbered at a slant, their silhouettes revealed
To me, in the moonlight, a village of tepees,
Their evening fire smoke drifting among trees
Leaning across a sagging woven wire fence.
In the air was a smell sweet as incense.

Oh, what a beautiful land, so serene it seemed,
The land where past and present were redeemed.
Farmers were finishing up their endless chores,
Shutting off the barn lights and heading indoors
In time to say goodnight to their children,
Telling them again how good they'd been.

They might even say, "We're thankful you're here,
For in all this world there's no one so dear."
But were they the farmers of the past or present?
Either way, their words were soothing and pleasant.

Really, I think I could hear whichever I chose:
The present made louder sounds; the past made echoes.
By then Robbie had long since fallen asleep
As Tony plodded over hillsides long and steep.

In the dark, luckily, the horse could see,
Drawing on daytime images from memory.
I too was drowsy after such a day
And gradually, quietly, to sleep gave way.
I awoke once when Tony paused with a shiver
And I heard what could have been a river.
Whatever had caused Tony slightly to delay
Didn't prevent him from going on his way.
I fell back into a deep dreamless sleep
And from Robbie never heard a peep.

Mum's The Word—And More

When I awoke we were home once more,
Suddenly sitting on the living room floor.
It was a mess, table tipped over and all—
And Tony was a rocking horse, wooden and small.
On his handsome face there wasn't a trace
Of mischief or anything out of place.
Daylight streamed through the windows brightly,
And we tackled the mess, no matter how unsightly.

I stood the clock back on its feet, so to speak
I felt I was dancing with it cheek to cheek.
It ticked off the melody of time arriving,
Of time leaving, and of time surviving.
Roman numerals told the hour to our eyes,
It was still eight a.m., to our surprise.
As Buddy said, time waited for us to return—
Naturally, that had been my biggest concern.

Robbie and I didn't say a lot that day,
We straightened up and put things away.
It seems we both thought we'd had a dream,
Vague, puzzling, maybe a little extreme.
Just how it happened, Robbie couldn't say—
What words of magic had begun our day.
Maybe that was just as well, maybe not.
Who knows where Tony might go on another trot?

"Should we tell Mom and Dad?" I asked at last.
"About what?" Robbie replied, a little too fast.
"You know perfectly well what I mean," I said.
But Robbie just rubbed Tony's head instead.
This was the way it was, and silently we agreed
To say nothing at all of our exciting deed.

And just in time, too, for in walked Mom and Dad.
As always they asked what kind of day we had.
"Oh, the usual," I said. "How about yours?"
They said fine and asked if we had played outdoors
On such a chilly fall day, at least for a while.
"Oh, for a few minutes," I replied with a smile.

During dinner (for scarecrows, "supper," I suppose)
Mom and Dad, in a moment they especially chose,
Said they had some really great news to share.
Our grandparents were coming from Delaware.
Well, this was a surprise, after all these years.
I almost blurted out, "Three cheers!"
I resisted, fearing my voice might betray
A hint of sarcasm, angry about the way
They had for so long denied us companionship,
To hide resentment, I just bit my lip.

"Yes," Dad said, "they arrive tomorrow, around two.
They're really looking forward to meeting you.
We know Grandpa and Grandma can hardly wait.
When they lay eyes on you and contemplate
How much they've missed all these years—
They will think you're the cutest little dears."

This made me feel a little better, I guess.
They too might have been living in loneliness.
Maybe they really couldn't get away before,
Now at last they would walk through our door.
We would begin a new journey together,
Its destination, family, each of us a feather
Folded into united wonderful wings,
To fly through whatever the future brings.

Then Mom added, "You'll just love Buddy and Pat,
They're the neatest folks." But after that
I don't know what she said—if anything at all.
I think I sputtered, like an airplane in stall.

Robbie looked at me and I looked at Robbie!
We read each other's minds. Could it really be?

We were speechless (but then, what could we say?)
So Mom announced another development of the day.
"Your dad and I realize it's not been right
Leaving you alone from morning till night.
We've found the sweetest woman you'll ever meet
Who said keeping you company would be a treat.
She'll come when we work on the weekend shift
Or when school is dismissed because of snowy drift
Or like it was today, for teachers in-service.
It would be good having someone with you like this."

Robbie smiled a grin as wide as wide could be.
He knew, and I did too, of only one possibility.
"I suppose this 'sweetest woman' once taught school?"
I said to our astonished parents, "She must be cool.
An English teacher, I bet! Who would ever think?
Well, we approve." I gave my brother a knowing wink.